East Lothian Library Service

C000180115

The Funny Side
of Living with A.D.H.D

The Funny Side of Living with A.D.H.D

A true account of what it's like to bring up an ADHD boy in a busy working family, school, holidays, nannies, heartbreak and success…

Ellen Nickells

Copyright © 2010 Ellen Nickells

The moral right of the author has been asserted.

Apart from any fair dealing for the purposes of research or private study,
or criticism or review, as permitted under the Copyright, Designs and Patents
Act 1988, this publication may only be reproduced, stored or transmitted, in
any form or by any means, with the prior permission in writing of the
publishers, or in the case of reprographic reproduction in accordance with
the terms of licences issued by the Copyright Licensing Agency. Enquiries
concerning reproduction outside those terms should be sent to the publishers.

Matador
5 Weir Road
Kibworth Beauchamp
Leicester LE8 0LQ, UK
Tel: (+44) 116 279 2299
Fax: (+44) 116 279 2277
Email: books@troubador.co.uk
Web: www.troubador.co.uk/matador

ISBN 978 1848764 583

British Library Cataloguing in Publication Data.
A catalogue record for this book is available from the British Library.

Typeset in 11pt Palatino by Troubador Publishing Ltd, Leicester, UK

Matador is an imprint of Troubador Publishing Ltd

Printed in Great Britain by the MPG Books Group, Bodmin and King's Lynn

This book is dedicated to everyone who supported us on the journey. Our thanks go to those who have touched our lives in a positive way and believed in Bart and us. My particular love and thanks to Liz who had to grow up with a brother like Bart and Robert whose quiet patience and sense of humour has got us through many scrapes!

East Lothian Council Library Service	
0933799	
Askews & Holts	12-Oct-2011
618.928	£8.99

WITHDRAWN

Introduction

This is the story of a family's determination to help their A.D.H.D. son succeed. It provides a personal insight into the bag of emotional pitfalls and laughter that they encountered on their journey.

A light hearted account of their family life together which features many of the funny situations they found themselves in whilst bringing up Bart.

"This book is written in the hope that it will inspire and reassure parents who find themselves with a hyperactive child. It is an honest, funny and sometimes sad account of the impact our A.D.H.D. son had on our lives."

Ellen Nickells was a career woman through and through, who finally decided to have children a little later than planned. Their first child was a girl, followed 22 months later by a bouncing baby boy. One of each sex seemed perfect, but as Bart started to move and speak it became clear that they had got far more than they had bargained for. Bart was diagnosed with A.D.H.D. when he was seven years old. Back then it was a relatively newly identified condition in this country and medics and teachers were nowhere near as familiar with the condition as they are now. Even today there are debates amongst medics and psychologists about whether ADHD is a real disorder.

Whatever the "truth" is about ADHD, Bart was a wild child - a cross between a helicopter and an avalanche. His behaviour could be so unpredictable and outrageous that his parents thought he would be kicked out of mainstream education before he made secondary school. Bart had "Trouble" written all over him. The moment he started pre-school it became clear that he was not going to conform and his mum was called in to hear about his short comings weekly. Bart did not fit the system; he was the odd one out.

If Bart was left to his own devices he would fail and could find himself in serious trouble. Some intervention was required but at the time there was no 'Dummies Guide' published to show the way. Medication was tried but wasn't as effective or safe as promised, so the family resorted to more natural methods to help manage their son.

A 'no blame' culture was set up in their household after an accidental fire, started by Bart, could have led to disaster. An imaginary tool box of solutions was created for defusing situations.

Bart is now 18 and has transformed through the development stages of wriggling baby, tortuous toddler and an easily distracted and somewhat wayward adolescent. Today he is a responsible and mature individual who is training to become a commercial airline pilot. The transformation is complete and is a testament to the notion of never giving up. It is fair to say it was not an easy journey; there was lots of frustration, laughter, tears and wickedly funny moments on the way.

The information contained in this book is not intended as a substitute for proper medical advice. If you have any specific concerns or questions about your child's condition, please consult the doctor (GP or specialist) responsible for your child's medical care

Chapter 1

Bart's school years were definitely not the best and the early years were particularly trying for us all!

Letter from St Thomas's school when Bart was just seven years old.

6th July 1998

Dear Mr. and Mrs. Nickells

I am sorry to have to write to you again, but I thought you should be aware that Bart was very rude to Mrs. Banks at break today burping in her face and calling her 'Miss Piggy'.

Naturally she was very upset about this, especially as Bart has been disrespectful to her on a number of occasions. I have dealt with his rudeness before but the message apparently has not sunk in yet. I would appreciate it if you could reinforce at home that Bart cannot behave or speak to adults in this way. I am trying to do everything possible in school.

Thank you for your help.

Yours sincerely

D Pascoe
Head teacher

Oh great, another letter to come home to.

"Bart, where are you?"

Fancy calling Mrs Banks 'Miss Piggy'; as if you weren't in enough trouble already at school. Although, when I think about how she looks…. no, best not go there.

"Bart, where are you?" Come here you little menace, what mischief have you got yourself into now?

I would appreciate if you could reinforce at home — What does she think we have been doing for the last seven years? Isn't it me who has to tell the school how to handle his behaviour – who is the trained expert round here?

"Bart, come here this minute!"

I wonder where he has got to. Both the kids are unusually quiet, normally they are fighting. Well just enjoy the moment.

I am trying to do everything possible in school.

No you are not. You have told me, in front of Bart that he is the worst pupil ever to go through your school. One of your teachers has told us he is mad! You say parents want to "get me" whatever that means and you don't work together with me. I don't think you have any idea what it's like to have Bart 24/7. You should try living with him, he would run circles round you!

"Bart, what are you doing with that suitcase? Where's Liz? What's that noise coming from the suitcase?

Oh my God Lizzie, it's OK, just let me get the zipper undone. It's OK, sshhhh. That's it darling, just take some big gulps of air and get them into your lungs. You really are a funny colour. Bart, what were you thinking about? You nearly suffocated her. Right young man, you and I need to talk!"

7 years earlier – "The Wrong Baby"

Unlike Liz, his elder sister's birth, Bartholomew Sebastian popped out easily into this world at around 9pm, 18th June 1991. I knew he was a boy as I had the amniocentesis check and he already had his name months before he entered the world. As a full-time working mum I asked the sex of both of my babies – so I could get everything organised -colours and all that stuff – up front.

Liz's birth had been a long and painful production and I was determined not to go through all that again. So I booked into a private hospital, asked who was the nicest paediatrician and took it from there. I remembered chatting to the doctor about gardening, my contractions were pretty regular and we were just discussing the finer points of pruning rhododendrons when he glanced at me – his eyes widened and he grabbed a white coat and mustered the two nurses into action. Bart was on his way out!

We never did finish that gardening discussion and only a few minutes later I was the proud mother of an 8lb 7oz blue eyed blond haired boy.

At 4 am the following morning I woke, slipped from my room, and went in search of the nursery. I stood looking down at this beautiful baby and wondered at the enormity of nature that enables you to produce something so perfect. A nurse walked quietly into the room and stood beside me. As I gazed into the sleeping baby's cot she quietly commented that baby Nickells was the one in the next cot. I glanced across and saw a miniature version of my father's face, resembling a shrunken prune, and thought, momentarily, 'but I prefer the other one'. Knowing what I do now, it may have been easier to swap their little wrist bands and take the angelic looking baby. Bart's birth was a cinch, but boy has he made up for it ever since.

The first few months were uneventful. Mum came up to help me, visitors came and went and all was well in my world. I had two beautiful children. Life was sweet. Being a full time professional working mum, I went back to work when Bart was eleven weeks old. We had employed a live-in nanny, nineteen years old and barking mad. She had a wicked sense of humour, had not finished growing up herself yet and was an ideal bridge between professional mum and children. It's not that I didn't love my children, but I had a job that I also loved and so started the eternal juggling of giving 150% to my job and 150% to my family.

I've never been good at maths, I'm more the creative sort, but even I can see that all that commitment didn't leave much time for me – or Rob, my husband.

In an attempt to establish a bit of 'me time' I took up riding. Mandy, my loopy nanny, had a pony called Kermit, (yes I thought that was a frogs name too!). When Bart was just a few weeks old I went out riding with Mandy. She rode a bristling thoroughbred, I was on Kermit and her mum looked after the children. What Mandy hadn't told me was that Kermit had a couple of unfortunate habits. He would walk past trees with enough room to clear his sides, but not enough room for my leg. A couple of times he chucked in a little buck, no particular reason, he just felt like it, and off I came. When we got back from our ride Bart was asleep in his cot – the perfect baby, Liz was toddling around and I could barely walk, bruised from Kermit's exploits.

Mandy was with us for nearly two years. She had a wonderful, sunny disposition. Always smiling, quick to crack a joke and incredibly accident prone. She was working for us before Bart was born and during the birth she went to Romania with her twin sister to help in the orphanages where many children had been abandoned. True to form, she lied about her age and told them she was 21 just so she could work with the babies. It was a distressing experience but that was Mandy – committed to giving her best.

Bart started to crawl at around 5 months and life changed forever. He had the ability to disappear – like the day he was contained by the stair gate at the top of the stairs. The landing had a wooden banister and vertical rails only four inches apart – Bart proof. I was busy painting the bedroom. I called his name and when I heard nothing I went looking for him. I hadn't heard that lovely baby chuckle in a while and wondered where he had crawled off to. But he was nowhere. Not in the bathroom, bedroom, not even in the toilet – although that room did have a particular fascination for him around the age of two. Where was he? How could I lose a baby and why was he so quiet? As I dashed along the landing I glanced down the stairs and suddenly I was racked with fear.

Somehow Bart had pulled himself up to the railings,

squeezed his head and body through and was now silently clinging to one of the rails like a little statue. I saw his head wobbling and those big blue eyes staring straight ahead. The drop below him was ten feet down to the bottom of the stairs. I leant over the banister and clasped my hands around him, gently releasing his fingers from the railing and pulled him to safety. Reflecting, I should have seen this as an omen but, luckily we cannot see what the future holds. I just hugged him and made a mental note to put up some mesh to contain him.

Chapter 2

The Early Years

Bart was a happy baby and toddler. I put a lot of this down to Mandy. I would catch them rolling round the floor together, Bart climbing all over her, chuckling and giggling. Having a young nanny had obvious advantages but one disadvantage for Mandy was the dirty looks she received in the local supermarket of "you're too young to have children".

To be fair she only looked about fifteen herself and we live in an affluent commuter area for London. Mandy careering around the local supermarket with one baby strapped to her chest and Liz in the front portion of the trolley awarded her some bemused and often hostile looks. It didn't help that Mandy was quite noisy herself and tended to chatter to Liz and Bart in a loud excited voice. One day she just let slip that the dirty looks in the supermarket were getting her down a bit. Her twentieth birthday was only a few weeks away and I planned a solution.

I commissioned a bright green jumper to be knitted for her by a lovely old lady with failing eyesight. When it finally came Mandy was surprised and delighted. It was several sizes too big for her in all directions, but the multicoloured words said it all. On the front 'I'M NOT THE MUM' and on the back 'I'M THE NANNY' made up for any size issues. She wore it with pride round the supermarket and we all had a laugh at how easily people assume the wrong ideas. Of course I didn't know then just how judgmental people could be. We have faced a lot of negativity about Bart and about my skills as a parent, but actually we are the winners and Bart's achievements to date and our relationship is testament to that.

Bart was not a "huggy" baby and was constantly wriggling to be free. Unlike my daughter who would lay contented in my arms, sucking her thumbs and twiddling strands of hair round her fingers, Bart would always fidget and tucking him in at night was more like a wrestling match. I would lay him down on the bed with him to stroke his head and he would be hell bent on shuffling around the bed and climbing out. From the moment he discovered he could move, crawl and worse still walk he was always off somewhere. I assumed that was just normal, but looking back I think it was Bart displaying his first restless hyperactive personality.

Aged two and three quarters Bart joined the village school nursery. Things started to kick off about his behaviour and our family life changed forever. We are a regular middle-class family; we live in a nice neighbourhood and have the standards of life that our parents, hard work and a good education have bestowed on us. The local nursery was looking forward to Bart joining them as they had thoroughly enjoyed Liz's company before. But Bart's first day was quite eventful. He didn't settle with the other children, in fact quite the opposite. By the end of his second week I was invited in for 'a chat'. I was not aware then just how many 'chats' I would be involved in during his school career. Like any concerned parent, I sat and listened to an inventory of misdeeds that my son had done. He had pushed children off the plastic slide, taken prized toys away from other children and delivered punches at several of the other boys and girls.

I was stunned by his aggressive behaviour to other children. The nursery made it very clear that we had a problem and we had to sort it out or he would no longer be welcome. I was confused as at home Bart was well behaved and just a bit boisterous, but once he moved into an environment with other children he just seemed to focus on what he wanted to do with no regard for the safety or welfare of himself or others. At lunchtime he delighted in flicking his food, fork and plate around. He played very rough in break time and it was not long before he had the company of a 'dinner lady' to make sure he didn't cause too much trouble. Yet at home Bart continued to behave well, growing into a chubby-legged three year old with a real impish grin and blue eyes that you could dive into.

Bart's mobility taught me very quickly that you had to know exactly what he was up to. Silence from him could only mean one of two things, he was up to no good, or he had wandered off. I must admit to being a bit paranoid about him disappearing. When we went shopping I would always sit him in the trolley, out walking I had a wrist strap – rather like a lead.

On one occasion we were waving off friends who had been to see us. As they drove off I looked down and realised Bart wasn't at my side. Where could a three year old get to in around sixty seconds? Robert and I rushed round the house searching in small places in case he was hiding. Then, when we were satisfied that he wasn't there we ran round the garden shouting his name.

We have a large garden that has a fairly main road running along the front edge and backs onto hilly woodland. We couldn't fence the entire garden so we had 'child zones' with gates and fences nearby the house. The hill and the pond at the back of the garden were out of bounds. We extended the search over our boundary and into the woods, but in my heart I didn't believe Bart, two and a half feet high could manage this terrain. After an hour that felt like a day, the 'phone rang. Bart was safe in a neighbour's house a quarter of a mile away. Apparently he had clambered over or under dead trees, through the woodland and come out in their garden on the other side of the hill. After that, I kept an even closer eye on him – he was not to be trusted. He wasn't malicious just mischievous.

Mandy nanny decided to move on. She had been with us since Bart's birth and I faced the upheaval of trying to find someone who could step into her shoes for the children and for us. Mad Mandy, who was learning to play the saxophone (even with several doors closed between us we could still hear the screech of that poor instrument). Mad Mandy, who, one evening just before she left, announced that she was a brown belt in some martial art or other. Of course we just fell about laughing, until her legs flew through the kitchen and several cups got broken in her demonstration. She was indeed a brown belt!

We started the heartbreaking task of interviewing new candidates. Anyone who has been through this process knows the upheaval it can cause to the family, It seems like you just about hold the juggling plates together – keeping up appearances at work and returning home shattered, only to start the night-job of being a good parent. Just when you have the routine almost sorted, it's time for change.

We were interviewing one particular promising candidate called Sara and Mandy had left us to chat whilst she carried on with the children. Next thing I know there was a terrific banging noise from the hall. I opened the door and found Mandy sprawled out on the floor at the bottom of the stairs. Her clumsy accident-proneness was legendary in the house and this was another example of her ability to cause total disruption when all I was trying to do was decide if the candidate was suitable!

We loved Mandy for all her qualities and traits and when she left it was like losing a daughter. She went to work with horses at a yard nearer her home. It may just be coincidence but several of our nannies over the years have left us to work with animals. I like to feel that we have been that stepping stone for them to move on to better things!

Sara moved in as the Mandy replacement. She was affectionately known as "Sawa" as Bart had a problem pronouncing his 'r's. Sawa was funny, loving and as gangly as a young colt, like she had never quite grown into or fully co-ordinated her limbs. She had her own car 'Fanny Fiesta' and as soon as I heard this I knew she would fit in. She qualified on the barking mad front!

As well as being great with the children, Sawa did a particularly mean impersonation of our Siamese cat called Shambles. She would walk across the room with her arms crossing over in front of her and her eyes wide open and boss eyed, just like the cat itself, who stared on unimpressed. Sometimes I'm sure that cat felt it was the only sane member of the household.

Life settled down, Liz started school and Bart continued to terrorise the other kids in nursery. At home Bart was always exploring and finding new things to amuse himself. I learned that when he was quiet he was usually up to some sort of mischief. The toilet held a particular fascination for him. He would unravel yards of loo roll over the floor like the Andrex puppy and one day I found him sitting in the toilet with his feet pushed down the U-bend and his face framed by the loo seat. He was fully clothed and very wet and I couldn't imagine how he had made himself small enough to fit into the shape – another Kodak moment in the bank to be brought out later in life when he got a girlfriend!

Bart was not always an angel at home. One evening we were invited to a friend's 40th birthday party. It was just along the road – walking distance and my husband's sister had been persuaded to baby-sit. What could go wrong, Bart was three and Liz was five?

We wandered over to the party and were massively

impressed that they had employed a butler for the evening who had an amazing memory for what everybody was drinking (small things pleased me. I was worn out from work and exhausted from my eternal quest to be a super mum) The butler must have refreshed my drink three times in around fifty minutes before the 'phone rang.

You know that feeling, when you illogically feel in the pit of your stomach that the call is for you? True to my instinct it was my sister in law talking incoherently and not making any sense – garbled words about tablets? ... In my slightly merry state I realised something was badly wrong. We raced back two hundred yards from the party to our house. Bart was milling around apparently absolutely fine – just looking a bit sheepish, but when Robert's sister took us upstairs into her bedroom and showed us a half empty pack of beta blocker tablets we knew we were in trouble.

Neither of us was in a fit state to drive so we called an ambulance. My sister in law couldn't remember how many pills she had left in the pack and Bart wasn't giving any information away. He had decided that if he didn't admit to anything then it would probably go away.

We were rushed to hospital in an ambulance, sirens blaring and one very excited Bart. He calmed down quite a bit and even stopped wriggling on my lap as a very stern doctor told him what a silly thing he had done. From what we could glean, Bart had only swallowed one or two tablets, the rest he had sucked off the sugary coating and spat out the actual tablet. Bart escaped with a rather unpleasant glass of 'charcoal' drink. At first he refused to drink it, until I whispered a few words into his ear and down it went in one.

Bart was put into a hospital bed, wired for sound and his pulse was checked every twenty minutes for the first few hours. Completely sober and with only the dress I stood up in, I climbed into bed with Bart and wondered how the party was going and what that wonderful butler was up to. Needless to say Bart slept like a log that night and I hardly slept a wink.

Chapter 3

(What a) Reception Class!

Bart graduated from nursery to the school reception class aged four and a half years. Knowing the trouble he had been in previously I was going to write a note to the new teacher to warn her of his behaviour. A friend of mine told me to leave it, as she was sure he would settle down. LESSON ONE – Always follow your INSTINCTS!

After only four days I was summoned to school and sat on one of those little people chairs, whilst the teachers sat on the grown up chairs. This was a position I would resume dozens of times during his two and a half years at this school. They explained to me that Bart would not sit still like the other children. He displayed little or no respect for the teacher and her authority. He would stand up and move about the classroom whilst the teacher was trying to teach and if he did sit down he continually fidgeted with anything or person to hand.

We agreed that I would talk to him about his actions and let him know that I didn't approve of his behaviour. This I did, time and time again. I would say "Do you understand Bart?" and he would say "Yes Mummy" and then he would go straight into school and just carry on as before. The first two terms were trying for his new teacher and very trying for us. The school interpreted his bad behaviour as a parenting issue, which made me sad and mad at the same time. We talked about boundaries in behaviour and I still didn't see the behaviour he displayed in school materialise at home when he was with us.

Bart moved up into year one and things got progressively worse. His behaviour became even more disruptive and communication was weekly if not daily, with notes passed from the teacher, via the nanny to greet me when I got home from work.

I remember one note asking for quite a large sum of money to repair the computer Bart had broken. Apparently he had posted a book into the DVD drive and the machine no longer worked. I was called in for another meeting and the teacher explained that he had been poking pens and pencils into any space he could find. I asked them if he perhaps needed a little more supervision. Their answer was to send him to stand outside the classroom door and Bart probably spent as much time out of class as he did in the classroom. Every time his fingers fiddled with the pencil and pencil sharpener, or he stood up and wandered round, he would be marched off to stand outside. I am not condemning or condoning this treatment but the net effect on Bart was that his learning was well behind the rest of his class and he couldn't read when most of the other children in class were reading books.

After the first term in year one I received a letter to say

that the school had asked for the Educational Psychologist to see Bart. I was appalled and felt threatened. I felt that they thought he had some psychological problem and, as he was only five, I asked to be present. I was refused, but allowed to meet the Educational Psychologist afterwards.

I don't remember much of what was said but I do remember her asking me how I coped with Bart when he did something naughty at home. I remember telling her that I told Bart "It hurts mummy's heart when you do something bad". The Educational Psychologist looked aghast. This was apparently the worst answer I could have given. According to her I was passing my emotions onto my child and I was warned from doing it again. From my perspective I was merely making Bart aware that we all have feelings and when you do something good it brings happiness and when you do something naughty it brings sadness. I thought this was a basic principle in life and relationships but I had not 'ticked the box' in this ladies eyes.

Bart's behaviour continued to deteriorate and my husband and I were summoned for a serious meeting. I knew it was serious as we were allowed to sit on the same level chairs as the teacher – we were equals, but not that equal as she sat behind a huge table to maintain her superiority.

She explained that they had run some tests on Bart, observing him in the classroom, at play and over lunch. She looked solemnly across the table and explained the results. Apparently 1 – 10 was a normal child, 11 – 20 was a maladjusted child and Bart had scored 23 – Go boy!

She scanned over her paperwork and I asked what this meant. She looked up over her glasses, frowned and said "malady" This was a word I had never heard before. My husband and I looked at each other and asked her what "malady" was. The teacher took a deep breath and uttered one word MADNESS.

So here we were, Bart was only five and a half years old and his teacher was telling us he was mad! I fought back tears as I thought about my little boy. My husband knows the signs from me when I am about to lose it. He bundled me into the car and drove me home. I raged and cried at the same time. How could what she was saying be true? On whose authority can a teacher in a tiny church school, with less than fifty pupils, be qualified to give such a slamming diagnosis of my son?

I drove up to the stables and marched down through the fields to bring my horse in for the night. She was only three years old and I had only owned her for a few months. As we walked back up the field together I shouted in rage and frustration about what I had just been told. The air turned blue around us and my voice could probably have been heard in the next village. I think most young horses, exposed to such behaviour from their new owner, would probably try to run off. Mine didn't though. She just walked along amiably beside me and looked at me as if to say "just get it off your chest"!

My horse would become one of my greatest confidants over the years and her stable was a place where I could turn to when I just wanted a quiet bolthole or somewhere to cry or let off steam. By the time I got home I was calm and laughing almost hysterically. The teacher's words had galvanised my love for my son and my protective feelings towards him were stronger than ever. The gloves were off, the fight had started. Step up, Bart and me in our corner and the rest of the world in the opposite corner.

My sessions at school increased in frequency. I had been 'promoted' to seeing the headmistress on my visits. She was a small, waspish woman, who power-dressed with slim suits and huge shoulder pads. Her facial expression resembled someone who had just bitten into a sour lemon and when she talked to me, she used the same voice as when she addressed her pupils, starting high pitched and finishing low. I can't pretend I liked or even respected her. She talked at me as if I was a child, she once mentioned that Bart's behaviour could be attributed to the fact that I was a working mum and I didn't detect any empathy with Bart so as far as I was concerned she fell into the 'opposite corner'.

One evening, I had been away on business for a couple of nights. 'The Full Monty' film had been released on video and as a special treat we all squeezed onto the sofa – G&T for me, lemonade and crisps for the kids – and we settled down to watch the film. Before the start I laid down the ground rules – "if you repeat any of the naughty words – you are dead." I was speaking metaphorically but both Bart and Liz knew I meant business. The film was funny on different levels and we enjoyed our precious time together.

Several days later I had the pleasure of another

summons to school. I watched as the head teacher sucked in her cheeks and blurted out, "I understand you have let the children see 'The Full Monty'!!" Her point being that Bart was now swearing quite frequently in class. I asked when this had started and established that it was before the previous Thursday when we had watched the film. I felt vindicated – she just carried on pouting.

I thought she was a humourless and judgemental individual. Not once did she sit down with us as parents and suggest that Bart may have anything wrong with him. She just made veiled insinuations that we had a problem. She told me that other parents from the school were so mad with Bart's behaviour that they wanted to 'get me'. This put the fear of God into me. I had a demanding job; I just about managed a family with some issues and now 'parents wanted to get me'! I felt at an all time low with Bart and the thought of meeting an irate parent led me to avoid collecting Bart, on the odd occasion I could, in case I met confrontation and aggression from other parents.

One day the head teacher called me in at her wits' end. She said that Bart was the worst pupil they had ever had through the school. She said he was a liability with no thought of his own or any other children's' safety. She said he could run out of the unlocked school gate – straight in front of a passing car – and she said all of this in front of Bart. I wanted to cry as she spoke to me, but I was more concerned about the ideas she was putting into Bart's head. I remember putting my arms round him as he stood looking crestfallen and completely remorseful. I gripped him and squeezed him gently with my hands around his waist. She couldn't see what I was doing, but Bart responded, moved closer to me and looked up at me in a knowing way.

During Bart's school career we would share many 'eye' conversations that only we would be aware of. Private looks, that brought support, love and comfort. Looking back at all these meetings I realise that whilst they distressed me and heightened my frustration with Bart about his behaviour, they also bonded us closer together. Every negative comment about Bart or me made me feel a greater commitment to fighting his corner and protecting him. We were always alone in the corner – but we had each other and our family.

Chapter 4

It Gets Worse

On the learning side of things Bart was getting left behind, big time. He was unable to read and I became very concerned that his future didn't look very promising if he couldn't read and write! I bought the "Thomas the Tank Engine' weekly magazines. Bart was mad about trains, something he shared with his Dad. Every night after work we would sit and try to read a page. For those of you unfamiliar with this 'high brow' publication, there tend to be a series of perhaps four or six pictures on a page. The story line is written beneath each picture in a rhyming verse which is two or four lines long.

Bart didn't like reading, because he found it hard. We could take between twenty and sixty minutes just reading four simple verses. Sometimes we would spend the first twenty minutes just reading the first two lines. It was excruciating for me and very frustrating for Bart. He would eventually read a verse and then we would just go over it again to make sure. But when he read it a second time it was all new to him. I thought this was because he wasn't getting the support he needed at school, but at the back of my mind I wondered if there was something wrong with his learning ability.

Nearing the autumn of his first term in year two I decided to get Bart checked out for dyslexia. It was a private assessment at the Dyslexia Institute at Tonbridge. It cost £100 and my mum offered to pay. I went into school and told his teacher, the head mistress, that Bart would be out of school as he was being assessed for dyslexia. I remember her staring at me and telling me that Bart was not dyslexic, he just had behavioural problems. I stuck to my guns – some teachers can be intimidating if you let them. But as their course of action was to remove Bart from the classroom, with no further look into the cause of his behaviour, I decided to take things into my own hands.

I turned into the car park in Tonbridge at 9.30 one cold grey November morning. I was seriously stressed with the way Bart was behaving. He was still very disruptive in class; his latest trick was perfecting a series of grunting noises that sounded like a pig in season. These noises came out of Bart in the classroom at all the wrong moments, when the teacher was talking or when she had asked for silence, he simply showed no respect to her, no matter how many 'chats' we had.

Bart had also started to behave badly when we were out. Recently we had visited my niece and her husband at their new home. Bart had been allowed to play in their back garden which led down to a shared drive behind a fence. We were milling around making small talk when a very red faced man marched up the garden with Bart in tow. He was ranting about his car.

Apparently he was accusing Bart of throwing stones onto the bonnet of his vehicle. Bart stood quietly and denied it. My husband defused the situation with promises that, if it had been Bart, it would not happen again as he would be standing with us at all times from now on. The man was still angry but slightly less red-faced as he marched off down the garden. We all breathed a sigh of relief and normal conversation was resumed.

The rest of the evening passed OK, but when Bart got too fidgety we decided to leave. On the way home he owned up to trying to hit stones on the guy's bonnet with more stones. I praised him for owning up, but chastised him for what he had done, explaining about paint work and scratching. We were never invited to my niece's house again. This 'only invited once' syndrome was quite common during his early years.

So here I sat, with Bart beside me, about to have him tested for something that might establish he really did have a problem. We went in and registered. They asked me questions about Bart, his birth, diet and behaviour then the doctor came in. She was a warm individual, who gave off a very caring aura. This, of course, reduced me to tears. I was used to coping with the snide comments from other parents and negative comments from the school. But here was a doctor who was being nice to me, it was too much. After I had blown my nose a few times and had a coffee, she explained that she planned to run a series of tests on Bart. She asked me if I had started my Christmas shopping and I replied no. As I was not needed to be present for the tests, she suggested I went down to the shopping centre and saw if I could find a few Christmas presents. I was overwhelmed by her kindness and wandered back to Tonbridge High Street with mixed emotions. Half of me was feeling elated that someone had shown me kindness and the other half worried about what Bart would get up to over the next three hours!

I needn't have worried. I returned to find a happy Bart and a calm doctor. She sat me down and started to explain about the tests. Apparently he had done quite well focusing on the first few, but as time wore on he became bored and stopped complying with requests. She ran around fourteen tests on Bart and for the last one she explained the task then sat back to watch what he did. After moments he had forgotten all his instructions and was spinning round on his shoulders on the highly polished floor tiles. He kept this up for some time. Typical I thought, always engrossed in the abstract thing that catches his imagination!

What the doctor explained to me was that Bart was not dyslexic. She did however highlight other possible causes for his behaviour. One was an auditory/hearing problem, one was to do with messages from his ears to his brain, one was dietary – what 'e' numbers did he consume, did eating certain things make him more active? And her last suggestion was that he might have ADHD. This was the first time I had ever heard of ADHD, I had no idea what it was or what it meant. All I knew was that Bart was now six years old, a complete handful, unmanageable at school and I was frightened for him.

I took Bart into school the next day and confirmed to

the head teacher that he did not have dyslexia. She gave me the annoying 'I told you so' look and I started to gather my thoughts on what – if anything – was wrong with my son.

Our second test was done at a local child's' clinic where they tested Bart's hearing and also how he translated what he heard into actions. They said it may have something to do with the transference of messages from his ears to his brain but they could find nothing wrong with him so we were back to square one. Meanwhile school chugged along with the usual monotony of Bart being out of the classroom most of the time and me being summoned for a weekly update on his bad behaviour.

That winter it snowed and Bart was beside himself. We had a great friend called Tony who always came to stay over the Christmas period. We had known Tony for years and he had been a friend of Roberts's long before I knew him. Though single himself, Tony embraced our children when they were born and played with them round the garden as they grew up. I think it was probably with tongue in cheek that Tony came up with the game called 'Murder' that he always played with Bart. it involved them running round the garden, Tony chasing Bart and huge screams and noises when they found each other and Bart shouted 'Murder'. This could go on for ages and it gave me a bit of peace inside the house to get on with the dinner and catch up with the washing.

But it was too dangerous to play 'Murder' when the

snow was down. The whole garden is on a hillside and the paths were too slippery. Tony decided to take Bart for a walk. Great for me, that meant at least thirty minutes of peace.

When they returned Bart was looking rather sheepish and Tony was looking very angry. Tony explained that they had been walking along the lane and Bart had been throwing snowballs. Tony had explained the ground rules – don't throw snowballs at people or cars – what could be simpler? A car drove slowly towards them and Bart launched a huge snowball that hit the car right on the windscreen. The car stopped and two huge guys started to get out. Assuming Tony was the father they gave him quite a bit of verbal abuse and helpful suggestions on how to be a better parent. Tony isn't a big guy so he just stood and took it whilst Bart managed to look sheepishly at his wellies. It didn't seem to matter how many times you told Bart not to do something – he still went right on and did it.

Things were getting even worse at school. Bart had moved on from pig grunts and was now making loud burping noises. He wouldn't sit in his seat for more than five minutes. He was constantly distracting other members of the class. Because of the time he spent outside the classroom he wasn't overly popular with the other kids.

It was quite rare for him to be invited to the usual round of children's parties. I do remember him going to one. Some brave mother had invited fourteen boys round for her son's birthday party. I dropped Bart off and felt anxiety rising round my throat as I explained at her front door that he could be a bit hyperactive. I felt it best to warn her but she seemed pretty cool about the whole thing. I went back three hours later to collect him. As I knocked and waited for her to open the door I could hear a huge amount of noise coming from the house and my stomach churned. She looked a bit frazzled when she answered but surprised me by saying that Bart had been the best behaved at the party and she would have him round anytime! That was a first for me – another parent giving my son praise. Perhaps I remember it so well as it only happened the once!

Bart seemed to be going into himself. He became withdrawn and he started to squint his eyes together. He would make noises and grunt as if he was constantly trying to clear his throat. This was a nervous condition which he displayed in and around school times, but was curiously missing at the weekends.

After the local clinic assessment Bart was referred for a paediatric appointment at our local hospital. They probed into the family, asking all sorts of personal questions about our relationship and how the family behaved together. I felt a bit resentful, they were only doing their job but it felt as if we were under the microscope as suspect parents

The hospital didn't seem to find much wrong with Bart. They seemed a bit baffled, but they did refer us to see a child psychiatrist, which proved very revealing…

Meanwhile Bart was becoming more hyperactive and he showed a complete lack of fear for his personal safety. One day I was in the garden doing a bit of weeding when I heard the start of the James Bond theme Dang dangdangdang dang dang, coming from way above me. He had climbed up to the top of one of the trees and was swaying backwards and forwards thirty feet off the ground. He had a piece of string tied around his waist and had attached the other end to a thin branch. He was keen on the James Bond films and I had bought him the series, so it was probably my fault that he was now about to create his own James Bond stunt. "I'm going to jump Mummy" he shouted. I should have panicked, but a feeling of calmness came over me. I had become very used to Bart's antics, climbing trees, swinging on ropes – I had seen it all. I just carried on gardening and, in what I thought was a fair rendition of the late Joyce Grenfell, I explained quietly that if he did jump he was likely to break something and that would mean we would spend all afternoon in hospital, I wouldn't get my gardening done and it would ruin the weekend. He sat up on his perch thinking about what I had said, and then he jumped anyway!

Luckily the soft Leylandii boughs broke his fall and he descended through the air with a series of grunts and hit the lawn a few feet away from where I was gardening. It may sound awful but I didn't rush over to him. I carried on weeding until he called out to me "I've hurt myself and you don't care" at which point I put down my fork and went over and cuddled him. I didn't want Bart to do extreme things to seek attention. It was my way of demonstrating that jumping thirty feet from a tree would not get the desired response. I explained to him that I had warned him of the outcome and he hadn't heeded the warning so he only had himself to blame if he was hurt. This sounds heartless but for me it was motivated by quite the opposite. I loved Bart dearly, but I was starting to develop my 'tool box' of responses that would defuse situations and maintain his safety. Bart had learned his lesson and left the more dangerous stunts to James Bond.

Taking Bart on a trip to the supermarket was another nightmare outing I dreaded. I was far happier to leave the children at home and battle my way round alone. I don't enjoy food shopping at the best of times and I resented how it always happened on the weekend, when I should have been relaxing or doing things I wanted to do. But buying food and eating is a necessary evil so off I would go on a Saturday afternoon or early evening. Bart was so badly behaved once he no longer fitted into the trolley that the security men in the local supermarket knew us pretty well!

Bart could take out whole displays of tins and packets that had carefully been built up as a promotional feature. I tried to hold his hand, not out of affection, but so I knew where he was. But that was difficult when you are trying to fill a plastic bag with onions and weigh them. I could send him on little missions to check the weight of the carrots or apples. It's amazing how creative he could be with a supermarket check weigher. He weighed parts of his body by leaning or sitting on it. He only put two items for catch weight whilst he held the other four in his arms. He would press the Brussels sprout tab when he was weighing pears – you name it – Bart achieved it and it could be very embarrassing at the checkout when the cashier noticed that the contents did not match the label

On one occasion Liz, Bart and I hadn't been in the shop three minutes when Bart had whacked Liz and they had set off chasing each other up and down the aisles, bumping into people and knocking two displays of canned fish over. The sound of the tins crashing to the floor was deafening and the looks I gained from other shoppers were too much. Something inside just snapped. I pulled them both to me, just round the corner by the tea bags so I wasn't in sight or earshot of any other shoppers. I growled through clenched teeth that, if either of them didn't settle down right this instant, I would pull down their pants in front of everybody and give them a smack. They seemed to know they had pushed me too far this time.

Like lambs they unloaded the trolley at the checkout and filled the shopping bags whilst I went off to the toilet. I sat in the loo and sobbed with tiredness, frustration and anger. I emerged a few minutes later to see all my shopping neatly packed in the trolley. I paid the cashier and she told me "I hope you don't mind me saying dear, but you have two wonderful children, we get a lot of rough kids in here, particularly over half term, but your two are really well behaved and polite"! She obviously hadn't seen me, behind the tea bags, just minutes before!

Chapter 5

The Diagnosis

Our first appointment with the child psychologist was a revelation to us all. Dr Fuller had asked for the whole family to attend. I had nothing to hide but Liz had school to attend so I didn't take her and just Bart, Robert and I went. We sat in a waiting room in what would have been an old pre-1900's house. The waiting room was quiet, no other children or frazzled parents on this day, and we sat and completed the questionnaire about Bart. "Does he sleep well? 0 – 5. How good is his attention span? 0 – 5. Is he lethargic? 0 – 5. Is he always on the go? 0 – 5. I think I scored the last one 10 as Bart was like one of those Duracell bunnies that never wore down its batteries.

After what seemed like ages, but was only about fifteen minutes, we were called into Dr Fuller's office. She was ancient and probably the oldest lady Bart had ever set eyes on. He looked at me and grinned and I shook my head vaguely to indicate to him that now was not a good time to be witty. If the comedy program Little Britain had started up a few years earlier they could have got a lot of their lines from our family. "Boy, she's ugly" was just one of many brutal but accurate remarks that could tumble out of Bart's mouth at the most inappropriate time!

Bart sat on his seat, swinging his legs, fidgeting with his fingers, face twitching, and surveyed the room and Dr Fuller. The room was old and drab with a high ceiling. The furniture looked like something from a house clearance job and Dr Fuller sat, legs slightly apart, in her old tweed suit and blouse. My heart sank; she didn't look capable of choosing a chocolate from a box of Cadburys Roses let alone making a diagnosis on my son. In essence she looked like a lady who would be more effective in an Agatha Christie costume drama. But appearances can be deceptive.

Give Bart his due, he just looked at her a bit quizzically then averted his eyes to the rest of the room. We had always bought the children up to behave well around adults – obviously this didn't transpose into Bart's school but, that apart, he was well mannered.

Dr Fuller started to ask us general questions as she referred to the form we had completed. Despite my first impressions she was in fact a very astute lady and it wasn't long before she was asking some very pertinent questions about Bart's behaviour.

It seemed that when he was with us he knew and understood the behavioural boundaries because we were consistent. We were clear with him, "If you do that you won't have the trip to Legoland we promised". This generally worked well as we always stuck to what we had said. All children push the boundaries as they grow up and realise adults can be easily played off against each other; ask one parent and they say "no", move onto another parent and they say "Yes". Then it's

"Daddy said I could do it". Robert and I got wise to this at a very early stage with Bart and we would check with each other to give the same response.

Dr Fuller seemed to respect us as parents. This was a bit of a first for me as most other people who came into contact with Bart didn't seem to respect me at all. She did a lot of nodding and writing as we talked. She asked us about Bart's behaviour at school, about his apparent lack of need for sleep, about his relationship with other children (generally poor) and his relationship with adults (generally good).

Then Dr Fuller turned her attention to Bart. He answered her questions politely, gazing at her with those beautiful 'butter wouldn't melt in my mouth' blue eyes. He said he didn't know why he grunted and made noises, why he fidgeted and was always on the move, why he disrupted the class and why he found concentrating very difficult. He confirmed that he had little fear for personal safety, like he would go into his own little world of commando fantasy when he swung from trees or jumped off high walls.

We spent about an hour with Dr Fuller and at the end she said she would like to weigh Bart and take some measurements – heartbeat, respiration, height etc. Finally she described Bart's behaviour as symptomatic of ADHD. Attention Deficit Hyperactivity Disorder. As she talked about the 'behavioural symptoms' my husband started to nod energetically. When she finished Robert said "But you have just described me as a boy" and he recounted, almost proudly, how one of his teachers used to describe him as being in a 'Perpetual state of Suspended Animation'! Dr Fuller explained that

ADHD is believed to be hereditary and six times more likely to occur in boys than girls. She also felt that Bart had a little ODD – Oppositional Defiance Disorder -and that he was displaying symptoms of Tourettes with his squinting and fast blinking of the eyes and his nervous habit of grunting. We agreed another appointment in a month's time and left. We were unusually quiet on the way home. I was busy thinking about all the big words I'd heard, Rob was busy thinking about his own childhood and how he left school the 'class clown' but with no qualifications and even Bart was subdued.

I remembered back to my own childhood. I had been caught smoking on a school geography field trip. I was summonsed to see the head mistress and I still remember to this day her saying "do you realise you are the only 'gal' ever to smoke on a school field course".

I remember thinking over her comment and replying "was I the first to smoke or the first to get caught?" I had meant this as a logical and polite response, she of course took it completely the wrong way and shouted at me for several minutes. She told me that I would not be made a school prefect as a result of my actions and insolence. I said to her that I was a bit like a wooden spoon "You can hold me down in water, but when you let go I will bob up to the top again". How rude she must have thought me, yet that honest analogy of the wooden spoon has kept my head above water many times in my life. There have been hundreds of occasions through my working life and being a parent where I could just have sunk but, something inside me always fights back for what I believe in

The day we learned that Bart had ADHD was like any other day. Something bad happens that knocks you off your feet, you go down, winded metaphorically or twisting with pain in the pit of your stomach. Then you think a while, make a plan, get up and get on with life.

I knew nothing of ADHD, so the first thing to do was to find out what it was. I did research and ordered several specialist books. Some were too heavy going and difficult to understand, but some books were just great. They talked about typical behaviour, techniques for dealing with the behaviour and also the drugs used to 'control' the condition. I found out about the latest theories of what ADHD was, why it occurred and how it could be treated.

It was very early days in 1990's for ADHD to be a recognised condition in the UK. I found much of the data I read came from America, South Africa and Australia where this condition had been recognised and diagnosed for some time. The use of Ritalin to treat ADHD was widely discussed and generally the benefits seemed to far outweigh what little was known of any side effects and consequences of taking the drug. But giving Bart drugs was not something I even wanted to consider at that time.

Home life continued to be a cacophony of laughter, tears, fun and arguments. I was pretty happy with life. I had a strong marriage and two great kids. OK, we did seem to have more of our fair share of 'events' but not knowing what happened in other people's homes I assumed this was just normal!

Chapter 6

Home Life –
Theft, Nannies and Fire

I tend to focus on the immediate needs and issues each day and disregard the peripheral so it took me several weeks to realise that money was going missing from our bedroom. As the children were quite small, Rob would put his wallet on top of a high chest of drawers at night, along with a few coins and his watch. He was the banker for the family and I just asked if I needed some money. But one day I asked for £20 and Rob commented that he thought he had more in his wallet than was in there now. He assumed, mistakenly, that I had just helped myself.

The missing money was a bit of a concern and I wasn't sure how to find out who the culprit was. I had a sneaky look round the kid's bedrooms whilst they were out but couldn't find anything. There was only one option – to ask them both outright.

I waited for an appropriate moment when Bart was on the calm side, sat them both down and told them that money had been going missing from our bedroom. I also told them that I knew which one of them had done it as I had installed a camera, so it was best for the culprit to own up, or they would both be punished. I gave them a few minutes to think about this and asked them to bring back to me what they had taken.

Imagine my surprise when Bart reappeared a few moments later with over three hundred pounds in ten and twenty pound notes, all rolled up in a little wodge. Obviously I hadn't installed a camera but I had caught the perpetrator. Because Bart owned up and had merely stashed the cash, as he had no way of spending it, he got off with a stern talk about the reasons why it was best not to steal. We had enough problems without adding theft to the list.

That's the way I remember it but It was Bart who reminded me of "the case of the missing money" which he still remembers. I had forgotten the detail along with so many other 'solved cases.' I found his version of events quite amusing and illuminating.

Apparently Bart saw the acquisition of money as a 'commando' challenge rather than theft. Bart recounted the means by which he used to acquire the money. Our house is old with creaking floorboards and ceiling beams that brace the roof. When we were asleep, he would climb onto my dressing table by the door and across a cupboard from which he could reach the ceiling beam. He would shin across this, in an upside down position and apparently this was the trickiest part of the 'raid'. At the other side of the beam was the chest of drawers where the wallet lay, so after helping himself, he shinned back across the beam and was home and dry.

He had no use for the money; it was just the thrill of the challenge. He remembers that when I saw the money my first words were "well Bart you seem to have stolen a small fortune, sufficient to go on a family holiday." He also still wondered where I had put the camera as he never found it! Whatever I really did say, the case of the missing money was solved and we never had a problem with 'theft' again!

We lost Sawa, our current nanny, after two happy years and, true to form, she left us to go and work with animals. She was going to train to be a veterinary nurse. She had given a lot of herself to the children; she was great with Bart's homework and had perfected his maths home work using bribes with sweets.

'Sawa' would sit him down in the kitchen, lay out the 'pick and mix' assortment and practice adding and taking away. Later Bart would excel at maths and I think 'Sawa' played her part in turning a subject that Bart found boring into a game. That was one of the biggest challenges – motivation to learn. Bart had got left behind in school, due to him being outside the class with the door firmly shut, and so catching up and keeping up was virtually impossible. 'Sawa' just made homework fun and she had such an expressive face and sense of humour that her enthusiasm was infectious – even for Bart.

But all good things come to an end and after a few false starts we employed 'Nessie' from Australia. She was over in the UK for two years and was quite brave but also quite young. On her first day in the country she ended up in a rather sleazy hotel in Paddington. The experience frightened her and galvanised her into finding a job pretty quickly. We were lucky enough to be advertising in a weekly magazine for a live-in nanny. Nessie applied and got the job. The kids took to her very quickly and we had a great couple of years together.

I sometimes wonder if having a succession of live-in nannies and me being away from home a lot has affected my children. But I believe that each nanny we had brought something special to our family. Neither Liz nor Bart was slow to read people and I would soon get some feedback from them if we took on anyone they didn't feel comfortable with. I did make mistakes with a couple of nannies, but they didn't last for very long. I was willing to give a loving home and share my family with the nanny, most of them still keep in touch and many are happily married with their own children now.

But during the time they spent with our family they became part of it and they were loved like an elder daughter. I once remember a colleague at work saying that her nanny had to go. I asked her why she had a problem with her and she said "Oh, no reason, it's just she has done a year and I don't like to keep them more than a year in case they get too close to my children". I was surprised by that attitude and how opposite it was to my own. I needed my children to feel stability and love their nanny, if the house was to be a happy one. After all the children saw far more of the nannies than they did of me during the week.

At weekends and school holidays I would always be the mum. Nannies were encouraged to go home, or visit friends or go up to London so that I could have my 'mummy' time. It's interesting that whilst we still keep in touch with many of our old nannies, and are very fond of them, both my kids tell me that they were always clear who their mum was from as early as they can remember, so I must have got that bit right.

The Christmas that Bart was six Nessie had taken herself off on a trip round Ireland. She was, after all, from Australia and she wanted to see as much of the UK and Europe as possible. It was the 23rd December at about 5.30 in the evening. Liz was in her bedroom and Bart was busy sticking himself and some balsa wood to the kitchen work surface. I had bought him a battery operated carpentry machine that could cut and shape wood. Robert had been horrified at first, after all Bart could get into all sorts of trouble without handing him a 'dangerous' toy. But I worked on the opposite principle that if you give a child something that has to be treated with respect, they will learn to give respect or learn the hard way.

Bart was as happy as a pig in muck with his battery operated device, his balsa wood and glue. I was happy because it gave Robert and I time to wrap the Christmas presents. Father Christmas came for many years to our house and the need for secret wrapping was challenging with the hours I worked. I had a long piece of Sellotape stuck between my teeth and fingers and we were about half way through the presents, when without warning, the whole house was plunged into darkness – a power cut, of all the times...

We opened the bedroom door and peered out. Coming up the stairs from down below was a terribly thick acrid smoke that smelt of burning plastic. What on earth was going on and where was all that smoke coming from? We had to lie on the floor and crawl down the stairs as the smoke was choking us. I fumbled my way down the stairs and opened the front door. A cold blast of air blew in, but there were no lights and we couldn't see a thing. We popped our heads outside the front door, drew deep breaths and then crawled on all fours through the dining room and towards the kitchen where the smoke was coming from. As I put my head around the kitchen door I saw a bright glow of orange flames licking the wall where the microwave had been. As I crawled towards the back door I heard a loud metallic 'clang' as the fan in the top of the microwave fell out.

I stumbled out of the already open kitchen door and gasped for breath and there was Bart hopping from one foot to the other. "Where's your sister?" I croaked. Bart told me that the microwave had caught fire and he had just legged it out of the kitchen and into the garden. We ran round to the front of the house, in through the front door and up the stairs. Liz was in her bedroom with the door shut and the smoke had not got into her room. She was sitting there in the dark. We scooped her up, made her take some deep breaths and bundled her down the stairs and out of the front door. "Where are the kittens" she cried, and I suddenly remembered that the two sixteen week old Burmese kittens had been asleep in the hall. A few more lungs full of breath and I dived back into the house, fumbling in the dark. Luckily the kittens were asleep on a bean bag near the floor so they hadn't inhaled the acrid smoke. I grabbed them and rushed out handing the children a kitten each and shouting "don't let them go".

I stared in through the kitchen window and the microwave fire had subsided, it had almost burnt itself out. There was just the odd trickle of dripping, glowing plastic and terrible thick smoke. Whilst the children stood outside shivering in the cold, Robert and I took it in turns to hyperventilate and run into the pitch black house searching for window keys to unlock the windows and let the smoke out.

We live in an old timber framed cottage and the keys tended to be hung on nails, dangling from the low ceiling beams – great if you could see what you were doing – but hopeless in the pitch black. With no lighting it was hard to fumble through the house, tracing the beams with our fingertips and finally clasping a window key. Then we had to find the window locks and unlock them. It took us about an hour to get all the windows open. Luckily we have a trip switch on the main electrics so the fire had just tripped all the electricity off. I contemplated calling the fire brigade but as the fire was out and the smoke was clearing I left it. After all we were only two days away from Christmas and I didn't want power hoses poked through the windows and a flooded kitchen.

What had happened, we asked as we all stood outside, coats wrapped around our shoulders and two kittens wriggling in the children's arms? It was only then that I remembered that Bart had been doing woodwork in the kitchen. Quietly I knelt down and asked him what he had been up to just before the fire. "Well mummy" he started, "I was making a boat and the glue wasn't drying quick enough, so I put it in the microwave to see how quickly it would dry it, but I was very careful, I put newspapers under it so that I

43

wouldn't get glue onto your turntable". I didn't know whether to laugh or cry, but one thing we didn't do was shout or tell him how silly he was. We had made a family pact earlier that summer to follow a 'No Blame Policy'. This meant that when Bart did something silly we just talked around the dangers of the outcome. That way we defused potentially volatile situations and protected Bart's somewhat fragile self-esteem.

The house stank of smoke for days afterwards. The burnt out microwave had to be taken to the tip, the Christmas pudding took hours instead of minutes to cook but we had a good Christmas. I sat chuckling to myself about Bart's battery operated carpentry gadget with blades. I was right he had treated it with respect. No cut fingers – just a bit of a house fire.

Bart was always experimenting. The episode with the microwave was typical. His impulsivity led him to act without thinking of the consequences, but he had a very bright and active mind. It didn't show itself in his school work which he found boring beyond belief because he couldn't concentrate, but Bart was very creative and imaginative. He had, from a very early age, always asked me "how does it work mummy?" questions that usually stumped me. They were not about ordinary things. His inquisitive nature had led him to take apart just about every toy he possessed. Sadly he tended to lack the enthusiasm or concentration to put them back together again. At first we found this incredibly frustrating, but you have to adjust to these children – they are all individuals and we have to make exceptions for them the same as they do for us.

Chapter 7

School and Medication

Bart had left his first infants school when he was seven, and went to the bigger church school that his sister, two years older, was attending. I went and met the head teacher before he started. I wasn't going to get caught out like I had when he started his first school. I wanted them to know up front about Bart and his history and behaviour. I also wanted to work with the school to help us get the best out of Bart and help them understand him.

The first few weeks were difficult for him to settle down. He had gone from a primary school with only about fifty children to a junior school with around three hundred and fifty children. I was worried that he might become a number and just one of the first years, I needn't have worried, Bart was busy making himself known amongst pupils and teachers alike, but it wasn't for good reasons, it was his attitude and poor behaviour.

I worked closely with his first teacher. She had around thirty children in her class and it was difficult to get time with her as I was usually up in London at work by the time Bart went to school and she was very often surrounded by parents on the odd days I could drop him off or collect him.

We arranged an appointment one day and she told me that she was very concerned about Bart's learning and his behaviour. I had thought he would settle a bit more in his new environment, but change for ADHD children can be very unsettling and lead them to be more disruptive and distracted. I had hoped that because I hadn't been 'summonsed' by the school that things were looking up for Bart, but they weren't. He was still very unsettled in class, lacked concentration and made noises at inappropriate times. He could not sit still in his chair and was up and about like a jack-in-the-box, sharpening pencils and retrieving rubbers he had pinged across the classroom.

His teacher had not contacted us because she had a much larger class and there was much less individual focus on him than there had been in his previous school. I viewed this as a positive, in that he wasn't constantly being singled out to be made an example of, but the downside was that his lack of concentration and learning would go unnoticed. The homework would come home and Nessie would sit him down to do it, but progress was slow. He couldn't concentrate and it was clear that he hadn't taken much in during lessons as he didn't seem to be aware of the subject matter. It was as if he was viewing sums or words to spell for the very first time.

We went back for our second meeting with Dr Fuller. We filled in the forms about Bart's behaviour and sat in the waiting room. Bart showed an interest in the forms and sometimes I would score him low on a particular point and he would tell me that he felt quite differently. We would talk about it and move the mark to a compromise position.

We also had to take a report completed by his class teacher and it was both saddening and enlightening to read her comments. Clearly things at school were a lot less good than at home. Bart's antisocial behaviour alienated him from the 'nice' kids and endeared him to the troublemakers. He found making friends difficult and the ones he did befriend were usually the ones that a mother wouldn't choose!

Dr Fuller suggested that we might try Ritalin to see if that had an impact on his concentration at school. I was very anti-drugs and it took a lot of persuading to make me allow Bart to take them. I read up extensively on the effect of Ritalin. Apparently it is an amphetamine, a bit like speed. If administered to a child without ADHD it would have a stimulating effect on the brain, but given to a child with ADHD it seemed to slow them down and allow better concentration. We were warned that some of the side effects might be loss of appetite, poor sleeping and nausea.

Although nothing was said by Bart's school, I felt under pressure to put him on medication. He was in mainstream education, but his behaviour put him on the delicate edge of what is and is not acceptable in school. I felt that if his behaviour sank too low then we would find him excluded or even worse expelled. I felt some pressure to 'do my part' by allowing Bart to take the drugs as this would make him more easy to handle for the teachers. I am not saying Bart was an angel – from a teachers perspective it must have been a nightmare to have a large class to contend with and then children with behavioural problems as well – but I am not here to make judgements, only to say what it is like from a parents perspective.

I finally gave in and permitted Dr Fuller to prescribe Ritalin. We would give him his tablet around 8.30 in the morning and pack him off to school for just before 9.00. We deliberately got Bart off to school a bit on the late side for two reasons. Firstly the less time spent milling around before school meant the less he could get into trouble. The other reason was that getting up and dressed for Bart was a feat in itself. It could take him twenty minutes just to get out of bed. Then he would sit there with his clothes laid out and just look at them. Getting up, dressed, having breakfast and getting out of the house could take up to an hour and a half. This was frustrating beyond belief for anyone trying to get him to school. My love and thanks go out to the nannies that battled the frustration of such a seemingly easy task each morning.

Bart started the Ritalin and we really noticed the difference. It would take about twenty minutes to kick in, then Bart would transform from being a frantic helicopter to a quiet, almost subdued boy. It broke my heart but I could see that he was much calmer and his school reports for our meetings with Dr Fuller improved dramatically.

One of the things that we weren't told about was the reaction as the drug wore off. Bart would come home from school quite quiet and after a while he would start to perk up and become more like himself, but he would also have terrible mood swings and he could get very angry or tearful. The school were much happier with Bart, as the Ritalin kept him on an even keel, but at home he was becoming a nightmare and very often his sister took the brunt of his mood swings.

Bart's weight and acceptance of Ritalin were closely monitored by Dr Fuller. They measured his height and weight each visit and probed into how he was feeling. As Bart's body became used to the Ritalin we found that it only worked for a limited time. It was suggested that he take a second tablet at lunch time to maintain the effects during school time. This in itself gave us a problem. The school would not administer his medication. They would hold them in the office and Bart would go and request his lunch time tablets but it had to be instigated by him. The big problem here was that AD stands for Attention Deficit which means they forget what they have to do. I could guarantee that the days Bart got a bad report in the afternoon coincided with the times he forgot to go and ask for his medication.

One solution from the school was to bring him home for lunch every day. The upside was he got his tablet and avoided getting hyper in the school play ground; the downside was it further alienated Bart from his peers.

Making and keeping friends was another issue. Bart attracted children who thought his behaviour was funny. This encouraged Bart to do even more outrageous things. Then Bart would get into big trouble at school and suddenly his friends would melt away – not owning up to the fact that they had egged him on – or perhaps not even realising they had.

When Bart was into his second term I had a meeting with his teacher and she suggested that it might be a good idea to look at taking him out of the state school and placing him in a private school. She explained that the class numbers were really too big to spend the time with him that he needed. She felt he would be able to learn more in a smaller class environment with more one to one teaching. I had always thought this might be a possibility so I started to look round at different schools in our area. I must have visited around five schools but three stick in my mind.

School number one was a stately home, set in acres of grounds; they advocated freedom of speech and actions and said they offered a 'holistic' approach to each individual's needs. We were getting on well over the tea and biscuits, until I mentioned Bart had ADHD. The two teachers talking to me seemed to step back slightly, with glazed expressions they made their excuses and drifted off to talk to other prospective parents. Clearly Bart was not welcome here.

The second school was a rather 'posh' establishment, with a bit of a Hooray Henry feel about it. I wandered round on the guided tour. Each student was immaculately turned out in their distinctive uniform. The cricket ground had been mown to an inch of its life and coffee in the main house was rather like a trip to a National Trust stately home. The headmaster looked remarkably like Tony Blair and his wife, coincidentally called 'Cherrie' stuck to his side as he worked the room for prospective intakes and fees.

The school fees were not cheap. It was in fact the most expensive one I visited. When my turn came for an audience with the headmaster I felt that they were doing me a favour rather than me being the customer. Again, we got onto the tricky ground of ADHD. Again I got a similar response. They made it clear that they didn't want troublemakers in their school – they wanted achievers. They talked about poor behaviour leading to expulsion – and I hadn't even signed on the dotted line! Clearly Bart was not welcome here. But I wouldn't have subjected him to their smug and cocooned society. All children are individuals, they don't fit a mould and the amount of money spent on an education won't yield results if the environment isn't right.

The last school I visited was very different. It was like a large house (which is what is actually was) with only fifty three pupils from age seven to eighteen. The headmaster was young and again I broached the topic of ADHD. His response was quite different. He seemed willing to entertain Bart's attendance at the school. I asked him to speak with Bart's current headmaster as I wanted him to be fully aware of what he was taking on. This discussion happened and a date was set for Bart to move schools for the next term start. I got the uniform requirements and busied myself getting it all ready. I drove Bart to the school outfitters, I wanted him to feel part of the process and I needed to make sure everything fitted.

When he was measured for his cricked trousers the shop assistant commented on how slim Bart was. I hadn't really noticed. I mean I knew he was small and slim but that was Bart. We ended up buying cricket trousers that fitted him on the waist and had to be taken up five inches on the leg. The total bill came to over £500 for his uniform, I felt light-headed as I handed over my credit card and reflected the difference in quality and price between this and Marks and Spencer school wear.

Bart started school at the beginning of the summer term. He seemed to accept the change quite well and I felt that I had at last found a learning environment that suited him. However after only a few weeks the head asked to speak to me and talked about Bart's behaviour and lack of concentration. He said he was disruptive in class – even though there were only nine students in the year! He questioned the dosage of Ritalin and said it didn't seem to be having much effect. Apparently Bart had been flicking ink covered rubbers around the room and one had gone out of the window which wouldn't have mattered much but he was on the second floor. The rubber landed on the roof of the headmaster's car. Bart had also been responsible for removing some ceiling tiles in the changing room and he slid down the staff staircase banister, which was strictly out of bounds as it was in the front hall with a forty foot drop to one side.

I had felt that Bart was getting on so well – and in a vain attempt to improve his behaviour and concentration I spoke to Dr Fuller and upped the drug dose to one and a half tablets. This was well within the limit of his prescription, but up until now I had been reluctant for him to have even the smallest dosage.

One of my saddest moments was when I saw his school picture. We tended to have one done every year and just put the latest one in the front of the picture frame. There was Bart aged three in a snazzy sweater with a little cheeky smile, then aged five and six with a boyish grin. His seven year old picture was very different. He looked smarter than ever, his hair was neat and combed, but his eyes were sad and drugged. It was his worst school photo ever.

Despite the increase in Ritalin Bart continued to be 'unmanageable' and was asked to leave the school just before Christmas. He hadn't even lasted one term. The head teacher said his staff simply couldn't cope with Bart and that his behaviour was causing other parents to complain. Bart was allowed to stay in school until the end of term. That Christmas I faced the prospect of Bart not having a school place, we had £500 of redundant school uniform and he hadn't even worn the cricket trousers!

We enjoyed the Christmas break then I went back to work with the serious problem of Bart not being in school. First I approached the one he had moved from and where my daughter still attended. They were very sympathetic but they had a waiting list. Then I visited all the local primary schools and talked to the head teachers. Out of two possible schools both had big issues with their year three students and neither school seemed willing to add to their problems by taking on Bart.

I started to correspond with my education authority. I made them aware that Bart was off school and that I urgently needed a school place. They were less than helpful and just sent me a list of local schools in the area. Meanwhile I employed a teacher on career break to give Bart some home tuition. I again contacted the educational authority and asked if I was entitled to a home tutor? A pompous man at the other end of the phone told me that I was not entitled as Bart had not been expelled from a state school, nor did he have any injury, for example, from playing sports, that prevented him going to school. I got so mad at his disinterested tone that I threatened to go home and give Bart an injury. "Would he qualify for a home tutor then?" The man clearly thought I was threatening a violent act on my son and started to stutter on the 'phone. Mr Pompous was deflating. I was only baiting the man and trying to shake him into helping us. I was doing all of this whilst juggling my job and the longer Bart was out of school the further behind he got.

Eventually after several sharp letters of complaint to the director of the educational authority, a letter to my M.P. and several hundred pounds on home tuition Bart's old junior school found him a place and he was able to settle back into the school I had taken him from to 'improve his chances and education'. When Bart eventually finished secondary education I was having a clear out one day and came across the school files for both the children. Liz's file was barely half an inch thick and this covered all her primary and secondary education. Bart's reports and correspondence, on the other hand, took up 4 full files – each three inches thick and bulging.

There were letters to the Head of Education at County Hall, several to our M.P. and a whole host to schools, different departments of the local education authority and various medical institutions. I threw most of the paperwork away, but I still retain some of the more amusing letters and reports, though at the time I had not found them quite so funny.

Chapter 8

All Work and No Play Makes Bart a Dull Boy

It was my mum's birthday and we decided to treat her to a weekend in Devon, staying in the famous Burgh Island Hotel where Agatha Christie had written two of her novels. Going anywhere with Bart was always a challenge that had to be thought through carefully.

On a previous birthday treat we had taken mum to Portmeirion in North Wales and stayed there for a couple of nights. The little village in Portmeirion is full of wonderful hiding places, steep cliffs and plenty of places to get into trouble. But we always set the boundaries. Have fun during the day then when it comes to dinner, we all dressed up and ate together – but this was the 'grown ups' time. Bart understood this concept and aged five I remember looking across the table at him curled up fast asleep in his chair as we chatted and ate our dessert.

When I tried to arrange our accommodation for Burgh Island the hotel said they were fairly full up and we were offered the boat house down in its own tiny cove. Thinking about the noise that can come from both children I snapped up the opportunity. Then the receptionist asked if we would be taking dinner? I replied yes, and she told me that the children would eat at 5.30 and we would eat at 7.30 for 8.

That gave me a couple of problems. Firstly I knew I couldn't leave Bart alone with his sister in the boat house unsupervised. They offered a child listening device but I didn't want to go into the whys and wherefores of that not working. Secondly my whole working life has been around food. I have travelled and eaten in many places around the world, always away from my family, alone, or with colleagues. When I am away with my family we eat together – food should be for sharing, fun and learning. Both my children had pretty broad food tastes and eating out together on holiday was non-negotiable for me.

I explained to the receptionist that we liked to eat together as a family and she wavered a little. She checked with someone whilst I hung on and then said she was sorry, they had an 'adults only' policy for the restaurant. I replied that if that was the case the family were happy to have dinner in the boat house and that both my children had been perfectly well behaved in other similar establishments. I dropped in the name of the Portmeirion Hotel for good luck and omitted that fact that Bart had ADHD. The receptionist was torn and she said she would 'phone me back. Five minutes later my 'phone rang and she announced that it would be fine for the children to dine with us.

When we arrived at Burgh Island both children were beside themselves and Bart was bouncing round like a jumping bean. We travelled across to the island on the sea tractor which blew Bart away.

We checked in and found that we had the most idyllic wooden boat house on stilts with a tiny cove and pebble beach and the sea. Bart was diving back and forth the length of the boat house shrieking with excitement. I pulled him to me and explained the rules. Have as much fun and make as much noise as you like all day (we had no neighbours to upset) BUT once it is dinner time you will be quiet and behave like a perfect gentleman.

True to form he and Liz charged about all day getting noisier and dirtier by the hour then, after a very necessary bath, Bart dressed in his trousers, a jacket and a Bugs Bunny waistcoat with matching bow tie! We had scrubbed up well and looked quite glamorous as we walked up to the main house for dinner. Traditionally they used to serve cocktails in a bar with a coloured glass dome in the ceiling. The building has a very 'art deco' feel about its design and people often dressed for dinner in 1930's style outfits.

As we entered through the French windows quietness descended on the room. It was subtle but noticeable. We were seated quite centrally and I glanced round the room. I received varying looks from polite acknowledgement to looks that said 'your children should not be in here'. I supposed that was fair enough, people had paid a lot of money to stay in this exclusive hotel – some had brought their children with them and complied with the rules of children eating first. Here was a couple with their aged mother and two children around eight and ten who were bucking the system

The waitress came over to show us the menu and take our drinks order. It's moments like these that I prayed Bart wouldn't start grunting, fidgeting or asking awkward questions. The waitress also looked a little bemused and I did catch a slight down the nose poise toward the children. We ordered and sat and drank aperitifs with two absolutely perfectly behaved children, Bart with his bow tie and Liz in a very pretty dress.

Dinner was in a large airy dining room with a pianist in the corner playing a grand piano. The children had ordered red mullet fish salad and a crab terrine with sun blush tomato dressing. They sat quietly and ate up every last scrap. They chatted quietly and didn't interrupt. After their main courses they polished off dessert as well. At the end of the meal the chef came out to our table. He said he was intrigued by the children and impressed with their appetites and non fussy approach to food. He asked them if they would like to inspect the kitchen during service the following evening and they accepted. I was peeved as I wanted to have a look at the kitchens but at the same time I was so proud of their behaviour – especially Bart.

It felt like following the chef's visit to our table we were suddenly accepted by the other diners. Couples were smiling at us as I looked round the restaurant. Outwardly I smiled gracefully (I hope) and inwardly I shouted Yes, Yes, Yes and whooped for joy. I had endured years – and still would – of people looking at me and making judgements on my parenting skills, or lack of them, and my son's appalling behaviour, but this one little victory was a sweet moment for me and probably impossible to understand if you haven't walked a mile in my shoes.

During this time I was also reading up on homeopathic help and supplements and the impact of diet and supplements for helping ADHD symptoms in a more natural way. I had read a book – 'The LCP Solution' by an author called Dr J. Stordy. In it she described the function of the brain with ADHD children. Basically, the theory was that some essential fatty acids are present between each nerve cell in the 'synapse gap', messages are passed along the nerves and they 'jump' between each nerve cell. It was suggested that if these essential fatty acids were in short supply then the message would take longer to be passed back to the brain. These fatty acids were also normally present in large quantities in the eye around the optic nerve. Lastly I learned that the front part of the brain can be considered as the manager. A simple example; someone at work annoys you to the point that you want to hit them. Apparently the job of the front brain lobe is to help reason out what effect different actions might cause. So for example if you decide to punch the person you might hurt your hand, you might hurt them, or you could lose your job.

In some books I read it was suggested that ADHD children lack the essential fatty acids that enable these messages to pass quickly through the synapse gaps. Simply explained, the individual might react or do something before the brain had a chance to work out the consequences. I found this theory fascinating as I had on several occasions watched Bart do some pretty stupid things and a split second afterwards his face would reflect surprise – as if he wasn't quite sure why he had just done that.

Being keen to understand a bit more before adding to Bart's tablet intake, I tracked the author of the book down and interviewed her over the telephone. She was actually in America at the time but I needed to feel confident about her theory before I increased Bart's pill intake further.

When she spoke she talked about studies being done amongst American prisoners in their prison system. This was in the mid 1990's when ADHD was not fully recognised in the UK and was seen as an excuse to cover up poor behaviour. During my interview with the author she also talked about the importance of having calcium and magnesium in their recommended daily allowance, as these two nutrients have been linked with the absorption of the fatty acids through the intestinal wall.

What I was reading about was much more natural than the Ritalin that Bart took, so I decided to give it a try. I read up on RDAs for the different fatty acids and minerals and I purchased 'Efalex' as this was recommended as having the fatty acids in the form that could be easily utilised in the body. It is worth noting that fish oil supplements are rich in some fatty acids but they may also contain vitamins A and D and taken in large quantities can cause a build up of these vitamins called hypervitaminosis which is harmful.

Bart was OK about taking the tablets, occasionally he would moan, but generally he just took them without complaint. To be honest I couldn't say for definite that they improved his behaviour and attention span, but he did appear to level out with no worsening of his concentration and I would often just continue with the fatty acids over weekends and holidays to give Bart's body a rest from the Ritalin.

In my opinion Ritalin was a necessary evil, a means to an end. It 'doped' my son sufficiently to subdue his behaviour and make him more 'palatable and pliable' for the education system. I was not keen on the side effects of mood swings though and we changed to a slow release variety as soon as it became available in the UK as this helped to reduce the up and down mood swings that Bart experienced as the effect of his tablets wore off each day.

Meanwhile Bart was back in school with his sister and they were giving him some classroom support to keep him on track in lessons. We started to work closely with the school, having regular meetings to discuss his behaviour and progress rather than reactionary meetings following on 'incident'. I think all children and certainly Bart have an innate ability to judge what people think of them. Aged five Bart had asked why a very close family member didn't like him. I had been astounded at his shrewd and accurate diagnosis of the facts. But, being only five, had done my best to assure him that this particular relative did like him, they were just a bit intolerant and grumpy.

When I could, I used to work from home occasionally. I had a very busy job developing new food products for Marks and Spencer and I rarely stayed more than eighteen months in one food area before being moved to another challenge. This meant in a sense that I was always learning about new parts of the food industry and applying successful techniques to develop new dishes and food products. My job was my passion which was just as well as I worked long hours every day, but I also needed to balance my family's needs and in particular Bart's.

One day I was working from home and I had a food supplier visiting me. I was looking after salads at the time and we were talking about the new developments for next seasons range. Bart must have been off on an inset day and in a vain attempt to keep one eye on him, he was in the lounge with me and the supplier – Deborah, who was a very professional lady – but also a mum like me. This was just as well as I was totally focussed on our discussion and it was Deborah who said "Ellen, why is your son up the chimney"? The house dates back to the 16th century and there are a couple of large fireplaces in it. Whilst I was busy talking, Bart had braced his whole body from one side of the fireplace to the other and 'walked' up the chimney. All that was visible was his feet. I called him and he slipped down followed by a cloud of soot. His face and shoulders were filthy and we had to have a fifteen minute tea break while I dunked him in the bath.

In addition to my family and my job I also had my horse. She was my late birthday present and I bought her on 1st April – April Fools day. She was like a third child in terms of requiring my daily attention, but she was most importantly my stress buster. No matter how bad the day or how much trouble Bart was in, when I went to her my troubles simply lifted off me and I felt that I was very fortunate to have her.

Chapter 9

The ADHD Support Group and a Few Days Away

I had got to know a couple of mums who also had ADHD children through Dr Fuller's clinic and the school. We decided to form a support group in our area for parents with ADHD children. The thing about these children is they seem to be jet propelled; they go on forever often needing very little sleep. They need constant supervision to prevent them getting into trouble that may cause harm to themselves or others. On top of all this the parent has to cope with the constant 'feedback' from school. My account of Bart's early years could be applicable to many ADHD children. Living constantly on the edge is very wearing and we thought as a group of mums that we could start up a support group where people had a chance to share experiences and mentor each other.

Because of the limited knowledge and awareness in the 1990's lots of parents were in the same position with no one to talk to about their issues. What we found when we met with other parents was that we all shared very common concerns. Behavioural problems, education, our own personal exhaustion, lack of understanding from others, either friends or relatives or school.

We advertised ourselves in the clinic, sent leaflets out to the local schools and invited people to meet at our houses on an alternate basis once a month. Gradually as the group grew we looked for volunteers to host meeting groups for different villages or areas. Four times a year we organised a large get together at the local school.

By now we had over ninety members with several satellite groups. We issued a quarterly newsletter with information for parents on different relevant topics like the school statementing process which is how to get recognition for the child's special needs and additional resource in the school from the local educational authority.

On one of the quarterly meetings at the local County school we invited the head master of a special needs school in London to come and talk to us. He had over fifty pupils and most of them had ADHD. He talked about a holistic approach to educating, where he felt that although medication has a place, there is a lot that can be done with the way you manage the child and their emotional needs. He also talked about boundaries – setting them out clearly and keeping to them. Lastly, he talked about academic achievement, something which most of us didn't feel our children would ever aspire to.

I was inspired by a story that he told about one particular student who had, amongst his qualities, a very aggravating voice and persistent manner. The head master owned up to being particularly vexed by this lad. He told us that years after the boy left the school, he was passing through the reception area one day and he heard the same voice, it was like déjà vu. He looked up and there was this former pupil, standing very tall and smart, in a first officer's airline pilots uniform. The headmaster was overwhelmed at this young man's achievement.

His speech inspired me. Although AD stands for attention deficit and for that reason these children find it hard to concentrate, most ADHD children that I have met are very bright and intelligent. They have as much potential as any other children, but they learn in a different way. I have seen this in my own son when we have shared homework together and revised for exams. Further on in the book I will explain how we approached Bart's studies and how we reached beyond goals I could only have dreamed of at that time.

That spring we took a last minute four day break to Iceland. With my usual passion for geographical land forms I was keen to show Liz and Bart fjords, geysers, lava fields and tectonic plates. With great gusto we hit Reykjavik on the Easter Sunday, having paid the taxi driver the English equivalent of £30 to get from our hotel to the centre of town, which must have been all of ten miles. It was a sunny day but the cars still had their snow chains on and the temperature was zero or below. Bart and Liz were racing round looking at the brightly painted houses with their steep corrugated roofs, wearing my fleeces and anorak. This was explained by a little incident earlier in the day when I had finally bundled them out of the house, counting suitcases and people to make sure we had all our bags. Perhaps that's why I didn't have my eye firmly on the ball, but the previous year we had taken a trip to Jersey to visit friends and only discovered we had left Bart's suitcase packed and ready to go in his bedroom when we unloaded the car at my friends house. He had arrived minus his toothbrush, bucket and spade, in only the clothes he stood up in. I wasn't going to make that mistake again.

That morning, on the way to the airport in the taxi, I did the mental checklist. Suitcase, tickets, passport, money, Robert, Bart and Liz – all present. As usual we hadn't left much time to hang around the airport, as this left Bart with a lot of opportunity to get into all sorts of trouble around the duty free displays or worse, perform his disappearing act as the flight was called. No, all in all, we were on target for a smooth transition through the airport, onto the plane and up into the sky.

As we headed out along the M25 I unzipped my jacket to let some of the heat out, Bart, Liz and I were wedged into the back seat of the cab and I was overheating a bit in my Iceland fleece layers. I looked across at Bart in his jumper, narrowed my eyes and said "Bart, where is your coat?" "I forgot it mummy" was his reply. I went into a bit of a tirade, here I was organising family, packing, tickets, taxis, entire holiday and the boy couldn't even remember to pick up his coat on the way out of the back door. "Great. We are going to Iceland" I shouted. "Why do you think it's called Iceland?'

I was ranting now like Basil Fawlty and the cab driver's eyes were wide and studying me from his rear view mirror. He asked "do you want to go back"? "No time for that" I replied, "we'll just have to buy something at the airport". After a pause, Liz piped up, "Actually mum, I've forgotten my coat too". I narrowed my eyes, glared at the road ahead and concentrated on my breathing. Didn't want to have a heart attack on the way to our holiday, after all...

So, this was Reykjavik, bright, cold, and very colourful with not a soul about. Where was everybody? We walked up the hill to the big church and a solitary cat wandered out from some railings to say hello. Apparently Easter Monday is a very important day for the Icelanders and they were all tucked up in their houses. The town was surreal and I half expected balls of tumble weed to come blowing across the street any moment. We got to the church but we didn't have enough money to go up into the tower to see the view. The taxi man had cleared us out on our short trip into town. We couldn't find a cash point and nothing was open. Eventually we found a taxi and came to some understanding about the fare home, which the hotel subbed us for when we got back there.

We stayed put in the hotel that evening and experienced their cuisine for dinner. I am not sure whether it was because we were out in the sticks or if the restaurant was typical but I can't say we overly enjoyed the food. Bart and Liz had been brought up to generally eat anything – this didn't, however, extend to puffin and guillemot, the very birds we had been watching on the shore line through binoculars earlier that day! We had seen the whaling boats, rusting and moored in the bay and the kids were aware of the history surrounding whaling. Robert and I are quite keen ornithologists. We always take binoculars on holiday in the hope we might see some new bird species and I suppose our natural interest had rubbed off on the kids a bit.

The fixed menu looked daunting, Puffin breasts with salad leaves to start and grilled Guillemot in some sort of sauce to follow. The restaurant was dark with lots of stuffed animals and preserved dead birds arranged around the walls. There was a smell that seeped out from all the taxidermy specimens and it was not conducive to building an appetite. We went for the a la carte menu, which added another £100 to the bill, but there are some lines even I draw, local cuisine or not!

Liz and I woke up the next morning to the sound of Bart screeching with amusement from the adjoining bedroom. He had woken early and decided to have a shower. The water was steaming out of the shower head and there was a real pong of sulphur and rotten eggs in the room. It was due to the fact that the water supply is drawn from the underground water table which, due to volcanic action, is warm and exceptionally smelly with lots of minerals dissolved in it. Liz and I looked at each other. We both felt we needed a shower to freshen up, but no matter how much shower gel we used, we came out clean, but smelling far worse than we did before. I passed on washing my hair for the next few days.

We did have a lot of fun in those few days. We went on an organised trip to see the Gullfoss waterfall which thundered and roared over the edge into the deep canyon it had cut. We saw geysers erupt from the ground and blow plumes of hot sulphurous water twenty metres into the air and we visited a beautiful church set in a remote and barren landscape, unoccupied except for a girl sitting playing a cello. She made an eerie, beautiful sound and we sat in a pew for a few minutes just taking in the rare tranquillity.

On the last day I had organised an action packed trip in the vain attempt to wear Bart out, so he would sleep on the plane on the way home in the evening.

First we visited the Blue Lagoon where we bathed, which was a most bizarre experience. We changed into our swimming costumes inside in stifling heat and braved minus three degrees outside to step across to the volcanically warmed waters. I had warned Bart not to run, but he still bounded across the terrace and did his 'bombs away' entrance off a rock ledge, taking out several other bathers with his entry. Luckily the water was deep enough, so he didn't cause any harm to himself or others, except for soaking them. The water was amazingly warm and we had to keep our top halves out of the water in the freezing cold to compensate for the heat.

Cleansed and bathed we made our way to a riding school that took rides out across the lava fields. The Icelandic ponies are quite unique, and their welfare is fiercely preserved. We had to disinfect our boots, collect helmets and then report to the corral where ponies were appointed depending upon individuals riding experience. Countless riding experiences have taught me to always understate any riding proficiency I may have, otherwise you can find yourself on something that has a mind to go fast and no brakes! It was a large group of about thirty or forty ponies and the instructors were quite strict. Bart and Robert had been given their ponies and so far Bart was behaving, in fact he was concentrating on being good. I thought how cute he looked on his pony and put my camera up to take a picture. As the shutter clicked the instructor started to shout at me, perhaps for safety – who knows – photography whilst sitting on the pony was not permitted. I was told off quite emphatically in front of everyone and as I glowed bright red I looked at Bart who, with a mischievous grin said "I told you to behave mum".

After that episode they changed my pony last minute. I am not sure if it was a punishment or if they thought I might ride a little better than I let on. As we set out the instructors kept riding back to me asking me how I was. Strange, I thought, to be receiving so much attention. After about a mile the senior instructor spoke out in her sing song voice "will the experienced riders take the track to the left, and the novices take the track to the right". Liz and I peeled off left and I looked over to the other group going right to wave farewell to Bart and Robert, but they weren't there. Now what had happened? The answer was, of course, they were behind me, having elected to take the advanced ride.

On the way home my pony started to play up a little. The instructor warned me to keep behind her but I wasn't confident that we could comply. About a mile from home the pony made a break for it and bolted past everyone. I heard her shout to tell me to just hang on and he would find his own way home. We shot off but after a couple of hundred yards I managed to stop him and waited for the others. I was used to riding naughty ponies and coping with Bart everyday left me with the feeling that I could handle any other challenge that life put before me. When we got back to the stables Bart was swinging on a tethering post and Robert was moaning that he would never walk properly again. They had switched to the novice riding group when we stopped by a lake for a break half way round the ride but the damage was done by then. Robert's jeans had rubbed on his legs from constantly bouncing around in the saddle.

The holiday was rounded off by a trip out to sea on an old cargo boat to whale watch. We were out for around three hours and the wind was bitterly cold. Liz and Bart were warm enough as they wore most of my fleeces. I, however, froze and spent most of my time wrapped in a blanket, kindly given to me by a crew member who made some comment about coming to Iceland without the proper clothing! We had first sighting, that year, of the Humpback whale and Minke whales and porpoises swam along with the boat keeping us company. Puffins and guillemots bobbed in the water and we managed not to lose Bart overboard which was an added bonus!

Chapter 10

Conflict With the Teacher for Bart and Me

Bart didn't respond well to change. A new nanny, new school or a new class group would severely disrupt him and focus and concentration would go out of the window. In this third year in junior school Bart moved up with his class to a new teacher. I think it would be fair to say there was a personality clash on both sides and the result was mayhem. His new teacher was quite elderly and very old school. She believed that children should know their place and speak when spoken to. She was one of those teachers whose strict reputation went before them and the mention of their name sends shivers up pupils and parents spines.

She had never heard of, or certainly didn't acknowledge that ADHD was a real phenomenon. She seemed to place the blame firmly at the feet of the parents and child and she was singularly without any sense of humour whatsoever. Bart, as usual, sensed her attitude and feelings towards him very quickly and spent the entire year in constant trouble, going out of his way to provoke and annoy her. It's very strange when you son is eight and you face this dilemma. On the one hand you can relate to your child's feeling of rejection and therefore understand why he behaves in the way he does. On the other hand you know you have to be adult about the situation and try to get your child to behave and toe the line – for his own interests and your health.

We used to have regular meetings with this teacher and she would always criticise Bart. She was never able to praise or take a more pragmatic approach. Talking to other mums we were not alone. It was almost as if to praise would be a sign of weakness and to criticise a sign of strength.

We instigated a day book that was completed by her or one of the class assistants at the end of each school day and sent home with Bart for me to read. I can honestly say that I dreaded coming home each evening and opening that book. There was rarely any good news in it, just a constant drip feed of negative comments, but in a funny way Bart's year in her class did us a favour. We became even closer as I aligned myself with him to try to improve his self-esteem, which was very low and certainly not helped by her.

Children can be quite rude in a personal way about individuals they don't like and Bart was no exception, in fact it was one subject he excelled in! Up until now I had always denounced such comments and tried to make Bart see things from other people's perspective, but this teacher was extreme and I found that if I was true to myself and honest with my son, I couldn't endorse her behaviour. I remember one particularly difficult meeting with her and the deputy head. She was reeling off a whole load of incidents and making judgements on Bart and me as a parent. I sat and took it for about thirty minutes then something snapped. I started to answer her back and when she started to shout over me I used the 'Christ' word in a sentence. I had never sworn in a school meeting before or since but I was absolutely at my wits end, exhausted by the demands of my own job and desperately trying to keep my head above water. The 'C' word stopped her in her tracks. She started to lecture me about taking the Lords name in vain and I wondered if some of the stronger words I normally used would have been more appropriate as this was usually much more my style.

I left the school and went straight to an ADHD support group meeting in the local health centre. I felt so stressed by her narrow minded, aggravating attitude that I felt like I was about to have a seizure. The head of special needs teacher from Bart's school was attending the same meeting. She took one look at me and asked me what on earth was wrong. My heart was racing, my hands were shaking and I was very pale. I told her I had just had the pleasure of a meeting with her colleague and she was astounded to see the impact it had on me. After the meeting I got a 'phone call from the deputy head, apologising for the teacher's behaviour and a promise that I would never have to deal with her again. She, however, had to deal with Bart.

The diary Bart's teacher had issued continued to cause me anxiety. I still have that diary to this day, tucked into a bedside drawer. Flicking though it I am fascinated to see the red writing from the teacher and the blue apologetic responses from myself. Bart and children like him forget things, they lose worksheets, don't write down instructions and if they do write them down then they lose the exercise book they have written them in! As a conscientious parent I wanted to make sure Bart kept up to date on homework – even if we had to stay up late to do it, but half the time I didn't know what the homework was that had been set. Bart couldn't remember and the exercise book or handout was missing.

It used to drive me mad. Here I was, an extremely well organised professional and I couldn't even hand my homework on 'Jonah' or 'The Romans' in on time. Calling Bart's homework 'mine' is a telling slip of the pen. I came to regard the work we did together as jointly owned. I would sit and read what we had to do whilst Bart bounced round the room, his Ritalin long worn off. I would not give Bart more medication after school as I wanted him to clear it out of his system. If he had a tablet after 4pm he could concentrate but he would have difficulty sleeping, so what we gained on the productive homework front we lost at night due to the fact that he could remain awake for hours.

One night I came downstairs at around 2 am and found Bart piling more firewood and paper onto the fire and puffing away with the bellows. This was alarming – he could set fire to the house whilst we were asleep. It was not unusual for Bart to get up during the night and wander around the house, but the regularity was increasing and I was concerned for his and our welfare. I made a mental note to talk to Dr Fuller about it on our next visit.

Bart's homework diary continued to cause concern and amusement in equal measures:-

Mon _ No P.E. kit (in red)
Tue _ No jotter
Wed _ No coat
Thurs _ Bart has been making anti social noises in class today
Fri - Would you please keep Bart's key ring with a bullet on it at home. Thanks.

And all this with a full time employed nanny, a husband who now worked from home and a dedicated mum – but it got worse:

Mon _ Playtime may have to be stopped. Bart has been squashing slugs in playtime and splashing mud on a boy's trousers. Flicking a dinner band in someone's face. Calling several people names. Please would you sign this. *

My response back was

"playtime is when Bart is most likely to get wound up and hyperactive. Unpleasant for the other children and the teacher after break as he will take a long time to calm down _ he needs to _earn_ the reward of playtime" signed 'Mum'.

Some of the entries in his diary made me panic – "Work to be finished tonight please" – what work? And it's 7.30pm now – I need a break and Bart needs sleep. But some of the entries just made me chuckle. "Bart disappointed me today by altering a word on the white board into an unpleasant word. What a pity!" No, actually that's great, Bart can read and has noted the similarity of spellings, Bart is creative and mischievous – he can make one perfectly normal word into something rude. Forget the content, Bart can spell, is creative and he has a sense of humour. Hurrah! I wonder what word he did create.

Looking back at that years teacher, it seems that in addition to no sense of humour she also used learning as a punishment:-

"Good illustrations in French. Well done.
But
Kicked Oliver (10 sums)
Kicked a tray (10 sums)
I suggest 20 extra sums"

Kicking is certainly not good behaviour, but a removal of a pleasure as punishment would have been better for Bart, rather than making him 'do sums' which he hated anyway. Punishing him with work just made Bart less motivated to learn.

On the last day of term I collected Bart from school and popped in to wish his special needs assistant a happy holiday. I was surprised to see his year teacher still in the classroom. She beckoned me over and since this would be for the last time, I went over and joined her. She handed over a whole box full of items that had been confiscated from Bart during the year. I was amazed to see the number of toys and knickknacks he had squirreled about his person and taken to school, only to have them confiscated. Perhaps the most alarming was his rather realistic looking 007 plastic gun. She smiled at me as she gave it to me. I had no idea he had taken it to school and there had been no 'incident' written up in the day book. Perhaps I had misjudged his teacher a little, maybe she did have a sense of humour tucked away somewhere and a knowledge that boys will be boys!

Chapter 11

Our First Big Holiday

We went to America when Bart was eight. It was the first big holiday abroad for the family and I had planned a route from Phoenix to San Francisco and hired a car. The only problem about holidays was hotel rooms. Bart couldn't share with his sister as he drove her mad and anyway she was two years older and didn't want to share with her brother. This meant that we used to split up the boys in one room and the girls in another. It was safest that way and meant that Bart wouldn't just go wandering out of the room. Managing Bart in his own environment was one thing, but managing him in a completely different country was quite another.

We took my mum with us to give her a treat and provide another pair of eyes to check out what Bart was up to! The holiday was great and just what we all needed. We drove up to the Grand Canyon for the first couple of days and stayed in a hotel on the South rim side. When we went to the viewing points around the edge of the canyon I kept a very firm hold on Bart. I didn't want him demonstrating any of his dare devil antics a mile above the canyon base.

As a special treat I organised for us all to fly around the canyon in a small six seat aircraft. Bart was not on any medication for the holidays due to my constant fear of him being over exposed to the tablets and my worry about possible long term side effects. When we piled into the plane the pilot asked who wanted to sit up front with him. My heart was in my throat as Bart jumped at the opportunity and wriggled into the seat doing up his seat belt before I had the chance to think it through. I thought about what could go wrong and my instinct was to have him in the back with me, but I issued some sharp instructions on his behaviour and let him stay there. It was probably the best thing I could have done, with the benefit of hindsight, but at the time I just sat with one eye looking out of the window, taking in the amazing views and the other eye firmly planted on Bart – watching his fingers for any movement towards any dials or knobs in the cockpit. Perhaps this is where Bart's love of planes started, for he has been fascinated by them ever since.

From the Grand Canyon we drove through the Painted Desert to Bryce Canyon. My second subject at college had been geography. I was in my element with all the different land and rock formations and I was sure that my children were as fascinated as me, so I rambled on about river and water erosion and the difference in the rock type and strata. My teachings were not very well received as my daughter gave up geography at school at the first opportunity.

To keep Bart busy on the long stretches between our different destinations I made him keep a diary. Primarily it was to keep him in a slight 'school' mode, where he had the discipline of writing and learning about things each day, but it was also giving him a broader understanding of the country, its people, climate and history and showed him that learning could be fun.

We only lost Bart once on the trip and that was probably our fault. We checked out of the motel at Bryce Canyon on the way to Death Valley. We had a long drive ahead of us and organising all our belongings into the car each day was my job. We paid the bill for the night and set off down the road. The car was unusually quiet. Suddenly I looked up and said "Where's Bart?" He wasn't in the car and his sister just sat smiling quietly to herself on the back seat. We rushed back to the motel reception and he wasn't there either. Frantic we drove back to our rooms in the vain hope he was there. No sign of him. On the off chance we knocked the doors of our locked motel rooms and one of them opened. There was Bart, mug of hot coffee in his hand saying "Where have you been?" I nearly cried with relief, as in my mind he had been kidnapped, but he was as calm as if nothing had happened. Apparently when we had loaded up the car, he left one of the room doors on the latch and had slipped back inside as we drove off. He had made himself comfortable, boiled the kettle and made coffee – even though he didn't drink the stuff. It took some time for my pulse to return to normal but Bart was fine. It's a funny thing but when your children annoy you, you wish they were someplace else, but when they are someplace else you worry about them, years on I have still to fully understand this concept.

The only other hiccup on that holiday was when we

booked in for the flight home. There were no seats available to sit together. We literally were allocated five seats in different parts of the plane. I started to panic, Bart would not last a ten hour flight from San Francisco to London on his own without big trouble kicking off. Who would he be sitting next to? Had they placed him near to an emergency exit – if so we might all be leaving the aircraft midway across the Atlantic! I needn't have worried however; Bart had been seated with a window on one side and a boy of a similar age on the other. They played for most of the flight and were fast asleep when we came into land.

Chapter 12

Good Things Come Towards You
When You Need Them

When Bart returned to school in September there was more change but, for once, this was for the better. His new year teacher was the deputy head. She was a warm and caring individual with a large bosom and a motherly manner. She called me in at the start of term, told me to call her Barbara and suggested that we have a formal meeting with Bart to establish the boundaries.

This was a new experience for me as the teacher had made the first move to engage me. Up until now I was always the one who asked for teachers' time, tried to forge a relationship and said "don't call me Mrs Nickells, call me Ellen". Now the tables were turned. Here was someone who was prepared to meet me half way and walk the extra mile for Bart and me. She said she had a strategy and wanted to work closely with me. She asked me to drop the 'Miss' and call her by her first name. She wasn't petty, she didn't pick Bart up on small issues and she balanced authority with praise.

Barbara suggested that she and Bart draw up and

sign a contract. We had agreed many plans with different teachers over the years but this one was a little different.

Point one was *"Mrs Barnaby loves Bart and will look after him and try to help him succeed"*.

The next points were:-

2. *Bart will not be rude to anyone in school. He will not use bad language anywhere in school.*
3. *Bart will be kind to the other children.*
4. *Mrs Barnaby will not judge without listening first.*
5. *Bart and Mrs Barnaby will always be honest with each other.*
6. *Bart will not behave in a way that disrupts the classroom and prevents other children from learning.*

and lastly:-
7. *We will have fun together and make sure our class enjoys school*

What a breath of fresh air! In seven little sentences Barbara had included the themes love, kindness, judgement, honesty and fun. I found myself actually looking forward to seeing her in meetings. She would always have a twinkle in her eye and that wry smile that let me know that she didn't judge Bart and unlike some of the other 'fossils' he had had as teachers, she exuded a sense that she was still young enough at heart to remember what it was like to be young.

Don't get me wrong, Bart was no angel that year, but he did settle down quite a bit; his behaviour towards other children showed some improvement and his self esteem improved from its fragile state. The school decided to 'promote' Bart up through the special needs register not, as I thought, in preparation to expel him, but in order to get him a statement for educational special needs which would entitle him to formal one to one support. The school had been supporting Bart with various teaching assistants and one in particular was exceptionally fond of Bart – her name was Gaye.

On one occasion my husband had dropped Bart off for school in the morning. We were between nannies and the normal working of the family was extremely challenged. I didn't feel that I could take time out for school runs as I then had to travel to London to work. I was normally in work just after 7 am and would 'phone the children as they were getting ready for school each morning. Every time I spoke to Bart I gave him the usual lines around "be good at school" or "see how well you can behave for your teacher" etc., the list of how to say the same thing in a different way each morning was endless.

On this particular morning Bart and his daddy had done the school run. Both Robert and I were very concerned about Bart taking his prescribed drugs, but if he didn't have any medication then he ran riot at school and we feared permanent exclusion.

Robert watched Bart shuffle to the front gate of school, subdued and drugged, as he made his way round to the playground. I think he must have been in a low emotional state when Gaye walked up behind him and asked him how he was. My husband is sensitive though not one for tears, but on this particular morning he just started to cry. Gaye was lovely and suggested they sit for a moment in his car to regain his composure. She said that Bart had reduced her to tears on more than one occasion. He was hard work to handle, it was usually one step forward and at least one step backwards and he could come out with some critical and cutting personal remarks on occasions. Gaye, like us, was committed to helping Bart, but it was not always easy when he failed to show respect or any gratitude. Interestingly, Gaye was with Bart until he left his junior school and we still keep in contact with both her and Barbara. I met Gaye some years later in the local supermarket. She asked how Bart was and, when I told her he was away at college fulfilling his all time dream, her eyes brimmed with tears and she hugged me and rushed off in an emotional state. Clearly knowing Bart had been a life changing experience for her!

Bart's sleeping was not good. He took ages to wind down in the evening and very often had a 'mad half hour' rushing round when bed time was looming. I tried all sorts of ploys including bathing him, reading him bedtime stories or snuggling up with him until he fell asleep. But the fact was he didn't seem to need as much sleep as me. He would often wake in the night and wander down stairs and get into mischief. On more than one occasion when I woke at night I went downstairs to find the front door open and Bart outside trying to find firewood to light a fire in the hall.

The following mornings were also difficult. Bart was hung over with tiredness, he found it difficult to get out of bed and ready for school and teachers often commented on him being almost asleep for the first hour of school.

I spoke with Dr Fuller about his sleep on one of my

visits and she suggested a small dose of Clonidine at night to help him sleep. At first I was completely against it, but all the natural and homeopathic remedies did not work and both Bart and I were suffering from sleep deprivation. In the end I conceded, got the prescription and gave him his first tablet. Liz was aware of my concern and we watched him like hawks to see if he had any adverse reaction. In fact after thirty minutes Bart just drifted into a deep sleep. I carried him upstairs, an action which would normally have woken him, but he remained fast asleep. He snored softly as I popped him into bed and tucked him in. I cried silently as I stroked his head. I knew that the reason he was sleeping was because of drugs, I worried about side effects and felt desperate that whilst other parents just said goodnight and their kids went off to sleep, Bart and I had pills to calm him down in the day and pills to make him sleep at night.

Chapter 13

A Little Flood and a Bit of Desert!

One of the things Bart loved to do was to come with me to put the horse 'to bed'. It only really entailed popping up to the stables to put a rug on her, or top up her water and give her an apple. One evening I was in the stable when Bart came rushing down from the top barn where several horses had their stables. He was shrieking something about water and the trough overflowing. When I got up to the barn I saw that indeed water was pouring over the top of the open trough, the ball cock had broken off and as the trough filled from the mains it gushed over the sides and was seeping across the barn floor and into the horse's cubicles, soaking their beds.

The lady who ran our horse yard was a mum like me, but she could be a little volatile on occasions. I quickly pinned Bart against the barn wall and demanded to know what he had done to cause this flood. His eyes widened in horror that I could accuse him of any wrong doing. He denied emphatically any involvement in the cause of the flood, so together we went to her house and knocked on the door. Her husband ran the farm and had just returned home after a very long day. I broke the news and told her the barn was flooding. To say she was not pleased would be putting it mildly, but I defended my son – if he had told me he had nothing to do with it then I had to believe him. Nobody else in his outside world ever seemed to give him the benefit of the doubt and in my 'no blame policy culture' we did.

The farmer managed to turn off the water, but not before several horses straw beds had been flooded and mine and Bart's ears were ringing from a bit of verbal abuse. In time the incident got forgotten and it was eighteen months later when Bart asked me if I remembered the flood in the barn. "Yes" I said, "what of it?" This was Bart's time to come clean. He owned up to bobbing the ball cock up and down to see the water flow stop and start. Unfortunately it had come off in his hand and realising what he had done and how it would be received he had denied all involvement. That morning I happened to be having a riding lesson with the yard owner. I plucked up courage, raised the subject and told her Bart was guilty. She asked me what my response had been to him. I replied that I had praised Bart for being a good boy and telling the truth, it had taken eighteen months for it to come out, but I viewed this as a step up in our relationship, that he trusted me to tell me the truth and that I wouldn't over react. Luckily we are still friends and have the occasional chuckle about Bart's escapades

That summer I had been working flat out and we didn't have a holiday booked. One lunch time I whipped out of my office and across Baker Street to the travel agents opposite. Before you could say "pyramid" I had parted with a large amount of money and we were going to Egypt for a cruise up the Nile in three weeks!

We all needed vaccinations for the trip and we were running out of time. Friday was the first appointment I could get at the doctors so when Friday came we all trooped into Jasmine, the nurse's surgery, en masse. Bart, Robert and I were over and done quickly and the remaining twenty minutes of the appointment were spent talking Liz round to offer her arm to the nurse. Liz hated injections, but not quite as much as she hated flying. Though she has never had a bad experience of either Liz developed a fear of both, which I was hard pushed to understand.

The following Monday I popped in to see the sisters in our health centre at work. They checked out the jabs I would need for my trip and said it was best to have them straight away. I was between meetings and a bit distracted so they gave the jabs and I felt pretty rough for the next few days. Two Fridays later we went back to the local doctors and after another fight with Liz we were all inoculated and ready to go. Work was manic and packing was left until the last minute, so it was only when we were relaxing air side at the airport that I realised with a jolt that I had two sets of inoculations, one at work and one at home. How on earth had I been so silly? I was losing it – all the more reason to have a holiday, but niggling at the back of my mind was the little issue of Bart on a boat for eight days, cruising up the crocodile infested waters of the Nile. Was this wise? Too late now just chill and enjoy a couple of drinks on the plane and relax for once, hopefully Bart will doze off.

We arrived in a very hot and steamy Luxor later that evening and spent what seemed like hours buying and completing our travel visas before we were taken by bus to the boat. It was good to feel the air conditioning belting out in the bus and the quiet after the surge of people at the airport, the noise, the confusion and one eye forever on the kids – particularly my 'little artful dodger'.

The boat was great, rooms on the lower decks, a very posh dining room and a pool and sun chairs on the top deck. After a quick look round it was back to our rooms for a well earned sleep. It was after one in the morning and we were being woken at 5 am – just four hours later to visit the Valley of the Kings at dawn.

The following morning we congregated for breakfast and found that there were only about eighteen of us on the tour from the UK, the other three hundred passengers on the boat were Spanish and Italian. Our group was the first to leave the boat that morning and we were driven up to the Valley of the Kings just as the sun started to rise. Bart was his usual hyperactive self, first onto the bus, first off – never mind anybody else! There were quite a mixture of people from different backgrounds, but with the exception of a honeymoon couple, they were all over fifty! I am not being ageist, but some snubbed us a little, particularly Bart, as if to say "we have left our children behind and we don't want to be saddled with yours". However Bart had a skill that would prove very useful to all of us on that boat trip.

After a very hot and exhausting first morning we made our way back to the boat for a late coffee and snooze before lunch. I was washed out from working too hard at my job, I was suffering a bit from the extreme heat and I needed to spend the first couple of days just sleeping, but with Bart that was not possible. The boat set sail just after the last group of Italians returned from their trip and Liz, Bart and I watched the crew cast off as Robert slept in his cabin!

Bart was excessively excited. I felt like I wanted to tie a rope round his waist (or neck) to make sure he didn't go overboard whilst my back was turned. We found our way onto the top deck and pulled some chairs into the shade. The mid day sun was beating down and there, invitingly was the pool at the front of the deck. I allowed the children to return to their cabins alone to fetch their swimmers. Liz returned three minutes later towel and swimmers in hand. Bart was some five or six minutes behind her, escorted by a steward. Having completed a full tour of the boat, racing down corridors, up and down stairways he informed me there was a gym, from which he had just been evicted! The kids swam until lunchtime and I read a book, one eye on Bart. The pool wasn't deep enough to drown in, as far as I was concerned, but Bart had perfected the art of water flicking with his hands and a couple of well aimed surges had hit two couples from our group already. I rushed over and apologised. I explained that Bart had ADHD and was a bit hyperactive – I always felt the need to explain his erratic behaviour, but I always did it quietly. Bart had enough troubles back home at school and I felt he needed to get away from them. He was also starting to realise that he was different in some ways from his peers. He didn't have many friends back home of his own age but, give Bart his due, he was well behaved and engaging with adults and I watched him building relationships with our group as the days passed.

The boat docked sometimes in the night and we would wake up early in the morning to see a new view out of our porthole. Trips to temples tended to be made either very early in the morning or later in the afternoon, when the heat from the sun was less overwhelming. The early starts proved challenging to Bart who was never good first thing. At one temple we had a particularly long and tedious introduction from the guide which tested most of us, but not Bart, he simply curled up on the base of a huge stone pillar and fell fast asleep.

When we returned to the boat we were late and all the other groups of Spanish and Italian ladies were already on the top deck occupying most of the chairs and sun beds and worse still the pool. Unlike our group who were here mainly for the culture, our European friends were definitely here for the sun. They had expensive swimming costumes, designer sunglasses, lots of gold jewellery and coiffured hair styles sprayed into place. The problem was that our small group couldn't get near the pool and we were all starting to overheat! After about an hour one of the couples called Bart over and the guy winked at me as he whispered something to Bart whose face formed that mischievous grin that I had grown to both love and dread.

Within moments I heard a familiar voice shouting "Bombs Away" and saw Bart leap from the side of the pool, forming himself into a perfect tuck before landing with a huge splash in the centre of the pool. Water went everywhere and the ladies who had only seconds before been standing cooling themselves, shrieked at the top of their voices – in a tone that told me that what they were saying was not very complimentary, as they dragged themselves dripping from the pool. As the water settled our group rose as one – with no given signal and mobilised themselves towards the pool. We had no problem getting access to swim for the rest of the trip, Bart would just dance around the edge and the pool would empty within seconds.

In fairness to Bart, he was not the only one to cause a bit of commotion on that cruise. I liked to think of myself as a secret smoker. I regularly give up and immediately buy a pack as soon as the next family crisis arises. I had deliberately not bought any duty free cigarettes as I had every intention of not smoking – once I had finished the pack. But I lacked the willpower and having smoked the last of the packet I went in search of cigarettes on the boat. I had made sure Robert and Bart were asleep after lunch and I took Liz with me on my mission to make sure she was safe. I had two problems, the boat didn't stock cigarettes in its little shops and I only had four Egyptian pounds on me.

I asked around and was directed in very broken English to the shore where we had docked. Wandering down the gangplank Liz and I were greeted by about twenty young children, keen to sell their gifts. I shook my head and in my best 'I am a Brit abroad' accent said "cigarillo, cigarillo". The children pointed to a single storey unfinished building about twenty yards away. We approached a wide opening in the building that I assumed would have doors fitted once it was completed. Inside we found a very small man with sun ripened leathery features, prostrate on his praying mat. I told Liz I thought that we had perhaps come at a bad time and we turned to exit. As we did so, he sprang up from his prayers, rolled up his mat and approached us. Liz squeezed my hand, she was anxious. In fairness, I am only 5' 5" and he didn't even come up to my shoulders, he also looked about eighty. I started to say "cigarillo" and he nodded his head and disappeared to the back of the room, returning with a plastic bag containing packets of different brands of cigarettes in two hundreds. He wanted to sell the full packs and I was trying to explain that I only needed one small pack. We started to haggle, with raised voices and I could see he was a bit steamed up by the way he was shouting at me. In an attempt to calm things down and bring a little humour I put on a posh voice and said, "Now look here young man" – Liz looked blankly at me, the guy stopped yelling and then the police arrived.

Unbeknown to me each boat had armed guards to protect the tourists from possible terrorist attack. They kept a pretty low profile and tended to position themselves on the top deck with their machine guns where they had a good vantage over what was happening. Seeing two tourist females leave the boat and enter a random building had alarmed them and they had alerted the local police who screeched to a halt in front of the building. Liz and I came out of the building to find three police cars and about twelve officers with their guns drawn. The guy in charge kept shouting "are you OK?" Lamely I replied "yes" as they escorted us back to the boat, but I wasn't – I hadn't completed my transaction and what was worse was half the people on the boat had come out to see what all the commotion was about and somewhere amongst them was Robert and Bart. This would take a little explaining!

We travelled on from Luxor by coach, to the Red Sea, with an armed convoy. Bart was very excited about the military presence; the rest of us just willed the journey to be over soon without event. I had chosen a lovely hotel complex that had three pools as I thought the children would want to chill out after their huge dose of culture.

On our second day there we set off on a tour to a protected coral reef where we had a camel ride and snorkelled around the bay. I took Bart with me and Robert swam with Liz. We were making our way into shore and Bart and I were just a bit behind. The water was exquisite, crystal clear and very warm. Bart tugged my arm and pointed ahead into the shallower water. There, in only about fifteen feet of water was a barracuda shark and what was worse was that my daughter and husband had seen it and were swimming around it to have a look.

I grabbed Bart's swim vest and protection and preservation kicked in. I made for the shore with incredible speed. I was a qualified diver and knew how to get the best out of my fins. I lugged Bart along spluttering as water went down his snorkel, but I wasn't stopping until we hit land. From the shore it must have looked like something out of a comedy sketch. I literally kicked until we were out of the shallows and almost completely on the beach. Only then did I turn round to see what tragedy had beset my husband and daughter. But there they were snorkelling peacefully into the small bay.

At lunch we told the guide what we had seen. Liz expanded on this and said they had watched the barracuda with his mouth open whilst small fish nibbled round the shark's teeth to clean them. The guide said we were very privileged to see such a sight, I didn't feel privileged, I needed to buy some cigarettes and I didn't snorkel for the rest of the afternoon.

As we journeyed back to the hotel Liz started to look a bit pale and said she didn't feel very well. I have always worked on the principle of "pull yourself together", not because I am heartless, but I could usually establish if they had a real problem or not. Looking at her I realised we did have a problem. Her temperature was rising and her eyes were rolling by the time we got back to the hotel. Our accommodation was one big room with two extra beds for the children. We had booked two adjoining rooms by special request – but something had got lost in the translation and the two rooms we were originally allocated were in two different buildings. After a 'discussion' with the manager we accepted one larger room with the extra beds.

I was concerned about Liz and now Bart had started to say that he didn't feel well either. I sent Robert off in search of some medical help and I bathed the children and put them into bed. After waiting for ages with no news I set off for the reception to see what was happening. My last instruction "Don't open the door to anyone".

Robert had made contact with the holiday rep and a doctor had been called. The rep was quite dippy and didn't seem to appreciate how worried I was. Robert ordered me a beer as I confirmed our flight departure to Cairo. When I had established that the doctor would be with us as soon as he could and definitely within the hour I returned to our room. As I approached I could hear Bart shouting and Liz screaming. Oh no, of all the times to have a row. I knocked on the door and Bart flung the door wide open and dived back into the room bouncing across the beds with a wild excited look in his eyes. Behind him, I saw a dark strange man.

Crying and shouting was coming from the bathroom where Liz had locked herself in. Pulling myself up to my full height I demanded to know what was going on. The man explained he was in fact the doctor. Bart had opened the door despite instructions not to and Liz had locked herself in the bathroom. The doctor examined Bart who I had managed to catch hold of as he raced round the room. He said he thought they both had a pretty nasty tummy upset and that he would have to give them an injection. Bart obliged by just dropping his pants and the doctor gave him the injection with no problem. He was used to taking medicine and it was no big deal. Liz, on the other hand, was a problem. I had to coax her to unlock the bathroom door whilst the bemused doctor looked on at Bart at his most hyperactive, cavorting round the room like a small wild animal.

When Liz finally emerged from the bathroom her face was tear stained and at the mention of an injection she started to cry and scream. I hugged her as she fought to get away from the doctor and his needle. She put up a brave fight but the injection was administered. I was just trying to salvage some grace by explaining to the doctor, who was looking suitably baffled, that Bart had ADHD, when a loud knock came from the door. Bart bounced to open it and in stepped Robert with two bottles of beer in his hands, grinning and with an appalling foreign accent he announced "Ello it eese the doctor ere". The doctor just stared wide eyed at me. I could see he was convinced that we were all mad and nothing I could say would deter him from his view – followingRobert's startling entrance. He completed his paperwork as rapidly as he could and he hurried off. Bart finished his hyper-half-hour and finally settled down. He had helped himself to an orange fizzy drink from the mini bar. I read the ingredients on the side of the tin – no wonder he was bouncing off the walls. Mental note to self – just water to drink from now on. Both the boys fell asleep quite quickly and managed to sleep though the whole night, whilst I sat awake on Liz's bed until five in the morning, mopping her brow with a cool wet flannel and bathing her every hour or so to reduce her temperature. The next twenty four hours were a bit of a blur but two days later we were all well again and we set off for Cairo to see the pyramids.

Our last three days in Egypt were as eventful as ever. We stayed in a hotel near the pyramids and met up with a friend we had got to know on the Nile cruise. We visited the famous Cairo Museum and found ourselves in the mummy room. The three thousand year old mummies were very well preserved and there were lots of funny comments and whoops of excitement from Bart and Liz. It was only on the way out that we spotted the sign that said "Silence. No children under the age of 12 permitted in this room". Oh well, we all make mistakes.

That evening I organised a horse ride round the pyramids for Liz and I but when Robert heard we were going alone he suddenly developed a keen desire to ride himself. Bart could ride but had previously 'retired' from the sport after being dragged along the ground of a cross country course with his leg caught in the stirrup. It rather unnerved him so he took up speed ice skating instead as he viewed that a much safer option.

Security during our visit to Egypt was fairly high. There had been terrorist activity directed at tourists and the government was taking it very seriously. We were collected by car from the hotel to go to the stables and the security guards took the details of the car and people we were travelling with. The roads in Cairo are chaotic, fume ridden and noisy – worse than Rome – and after a ten minute journey for which I had my eyes tightly shut, we arrived at a building with a gate off to the side where the horses were kept. We were invited in for water and found ourselves in a perfume parlour, but it was obviously run by a bit of an entrepreneur who did perfume as a little business on the side! We managed to escape the parlour with the promise that we would look after the ride.

The first part of the ride was through the bustling streets I had just journeyed through with my eyes closed. Bart and Liz were behind me and Robert was keeping an eye on them from the back. When we reached the gateway that leads to the pyramids I was relieved that we had left the traffic behind and then instantly alarmed to see a dead horse on a rubbish tip to our left, still in rigour with its legs sticking up in the air. My first thought was to divert the children's attention, particularly Liz who adored horses. I waffled on about "if we look carefully to the right we should get our first view of the pyramids". It worked with Bart and Robert, but as I repeated it for the third time Liz said quietly "it's all right mummy, I've seen it".

Our guide took us quite a long route that seemed to go parallel with the pyramids but after a while they seemed to recede off to our right and he was keen for us to follow him up a wadi off to the left. I had been warned about these tactics before I left the UK and I had no intention of following this man into a wadi to meet his family or worse. I whispered to the kids and announced "Family turn right" which we all did together, leaving the guide alone trotting up the wadi talking to himself. He eventually caught up with us as we were walking round the furthest pyramid. His English was limited and my Egyptian was zero so I just smiled, waved and said "Hi". The rest of the ride was uneventful if you discount Robert's first attempt at canter. We all took off as our guide kept shouting "Gallop – yes? Gallop" I kept back with Robert and was alarmed to see that as he increased speed he began to wobble alarmingly in the saddle. "Sit back" I shouted as he leaned forward but he was all right, the pony was so small and he is tall, he just let his legs hang down like a pair of stabilisers on a bike.

It was our last night in Egypt. We had a lovely two

bedroom apartment with twin beds. Liz and Robert were tired and they went off to bed leaving me and my 'bouncing bean' to pack. I had poured myself a large gin and tonic and Bart was admiring the resin statue of Tutankhamen that I had haggled for in the souk earlier in the day. With most of the packing complete I laid down on my bed with my book whilst Bart continued to fiddle with Tut. Out of the corner of my eye I saw something crawling across the middle of the room on the bedroom carpet. It hadn't escaped Bart's attention either and he was off the bed like a shot. I shouted to him not to touch whatever it was and went in search of my empty gin glass. As I came out of the bathroom I saw it making its way across the room. It was only a couple of feet from the open suitcases. Bart dived for the little creature and flicked it from behind with his fingers. It flew up into the air and landed almost in front of me. I pushed it into my glass with a postcard and pressed it firmly down. It looked like a tiny pink or orange prawn, but as we both gazed at it through the glass Bart said "Mummy, why has it brought its tail up over its head?" "Because it's a scorpion" I said! I thought scorpions were big – about three or four inches long, not just one inch as this one was.

We debated what to do with it and settled on opening the French windows and launching it over the side of our balcony to the path below. This done, we climbed into our beds and I put the light out. After a while Bart said "Mummy, that scorpion was very small. Do you think it is a baby and it has a mummy and daddy and some brothers and sisters?" With that thought in mind I told Bart not to get up for the loo in the middle of the night and if he really wanted to go he must wake me.

The following morning we were on our way to the airport with our guide on the coach. Being keen on nature and reflecting on Bart's question about babies I decided to ask the guide what sort of scorpion it was. He kept nodding his head and saying was it black or red? I kept telling him it was a pinky orange cooked prawn colour, but I wasn't making myself clear so I grabbed hold of something that had the colour I was trying to describe and showed him. The guide went quiet and actually paled. He asked again where I had seen it and Robert and Liz became interested. Apparently our 'room mate' was a small but deadly variety of scorpion that often claimed the lives of small children in Bedouin camps. He told us that they are completely blind and use heat to sense where other bodies are. Because Bart had rushed out of nowhere and flicked him up from behind, the scorpion had no chance to react (thank goodness) and had been safely captured into my G+T glass. The guide asked how I had disposed on it and I reflected that I had launched it out of the window, trying to recall if anybody was passing at the time. Robert demanded to know why I hadn't woken him and told me he would have worried all night if he had known. "It was precisely because you would worry that I didn't wake you up" I replied. Honestly Men!

Chapter 14

A New School Year and Nanny Trouble

Bart returned into school well, he was much more settled now. By writing daily in his Egyptian diary he had kept his concentration levels for studying awake and it was not so difficult to return to the confines of the classroom. Because Bart was more settled he was less restless. He had started to form some friendships with other children in his year and also seemed to be getting on far better with most of his teachers. They studied the Egyptians that term and for once in Bart's life he actually knew about something without having to read pages and pages or listen intently. He took his holiday diary into school and gave a little talk about what he had seen. Although those who were exposed to Bart saw him as a very 'in your face' individual, he was, in fact, quite shy and would never brag about what he had done or seen. He was so modest that it was only when I was in school and I asked the teacher if he had told her about his holiday that she realised he had been to Egypt.

Travel for us as a family had many benefits. We were a proper family unit with no nannies around. Much as I loved most of them it was good to be just a family. I got to spend concentrated 'special time' with the children and the weekly pressures of work were absent.

Nessie, our Australian nanny, stayed with us for nearly two years, but eventually it was time for her to return to Oz and we started to look for a new nanny. The film 'Mrs Doubtfire' was a family favourite and I had a notion that it might be a good idea to employ a more mature person who would have more of life's experiences under her belt. We interviewed one lady who seemed perfect, her name was Enid. She was a 'young' grandmother with two boys of her own and I had visions of her bustling round the house with the Hoover to the strains of Queen – 'I want to break free'.

Interviews are very different from when a person lives with you as I found out in this instance. Enid moved in and set about making herself at home. She was in her late fifties and I took this into account when she didn't sometimes grasp what I had said the first time (or the second for that matter). The children had learnt to be very discerning on the nanny front. They were quick to judge and usually bang on with their first impressions. I soon became aware that I hadn't employed the second Mrs Doubtfire – but a rather strange lady who was quite insecure and insular.

Although she had feigned affection for Bart and Liz on her interview, that affection did not move in when she did. She didn't listen to the children, couldn't cope with Bart and Liz who disliked her intensely. She had big glasses with thick lenses that made her eyes appear twice their normal size and she would just stare at you as you spoke to her. It didn't take any of us – apart from Enid – to know in a very few days that things were not going to work out. Letters were written daily from the school informing us that Bart had no pencil case, school books, P.E. kit etc. with him. Enid flustered around me and when she spoke she seemed to move completely into my space with her face only a few inches away from mine. Robert could see trouble looming and kept a wide berth – just passing the time of day if he met her round the house. Bart and Liz were late for school every day and when I raised this she blamed Bart. I resented this as I had gone to great lengths to talk about Bart's behaviour and ADHD in her two interviews and having your own child blamed when you were employing someone to help was too much.

Things came to a head on the Friday of her second week. I was working from home and desperate to get my head down and get on with the tasks I had set myself. I offered to do the school run in an attempt to get the children in on time for one day in the week. On the way home I realised that I couldn't work with her twittering on around me so I popped into the house, collected my 'phone and computer and went and parked at the stables and worked in the car.

After about two hours of 'phone calls and e-mails I realised that I was putting off going home. Robert was out working and I didn't want to be in my own house with her – even though I had always regarded my home as my sanctuary. Regretfully I started the car up and headed home. I had only been in the house for ten minutes when she came and found me. She started to go on about her life and the fact that her husband, a vicar, had left her. What a wise man I thought! She talked about raising her children on her own, how unpleasant her ex husband was and then she flipped into a conversation about my own husband and accused him of mental bullying. I was stunned. No one who knows my husband would ever imagine he was capable of such a thing. He is good natured, naturally funny and avoids all conflict like the plague. I asked her what she meant by her accusations and she started to ramble in a confused manner mixing my own husband up with hers.

Enough! I thought, she then proceeded to inform me she was working over seventy hours a week – Monday to Friday and asked me what I was going to do about it? Luckily we have always had contracts for our nannies and her hours and duties were clearly laid down on paper. I explained that once the children were at school she had the rest of the day virtually to herself until she picked them up again. She was contracted to do a weekly food shop and light cleaning round the house. When I mentioned cleaning she said she had never done it and could she apply to go on a course? That was enough for me. I informed her if she didn't like the job she was free to leave. She seemed to rethink her options and announced she wanted to stay as she had a dentist appointment and her car was going into the garage for a service the following week! But by then the damage was done. She was the only nanny I have told to leave the house. I told her that as she was in her probationary period she could stay for one more week, then I took my work and decamped out into the garden.

Our house is full of incidents, surprises, accidents,

laughter and love. Enid was disturbing the atmosphere and people in it and she had to go. I would rather be without help and feel in harmony, than share my roof with someone who undermined the foundations of our family.

Lovely 'Lorry Lorraine' nanny came along shortly afterwards and she certainly fits into my 'most loved' category for nannies. She had been doing various jobs that hadn't worked out for her and she had decided to train to be a teacher, but she wanted some experience of children before she applied. Well if she wanted experience she had come to the right family. She moved in and after their previous experience Bart and Liz took to her immediately. She was great with organising Bart and very patient and supportive to them both. Her nature was such that most events simply slid over the top of her head. She didn't dramatise events and she became very popular at the school which was a real bonus for our family!

One evening I was returning from work. It was about 6.30 and Robert had just collected me from the station and was driving me home. It was swimming night for the children and we passed each other on the way. As their car approached I noticed something sticking out of the rear window. 'Lorry' sailed past, focussed on the road ahead with a beamy smile on her face. Bart sat in the back, with his window wound down, his arm extended like a periscope and his single middle finger held high for all to see!

When they returned home later that evening I asked if she had seen us pass. "No" she said. I asked Bart what he was doing showing his middle finger to the world as he went by. He looked sheepish and we agreed that he wouldn't do that again. I never saw a repeat performance but that doesn't mean he didn't do it.

Lorry, unlike Enid, managed to pack loads into her days. She often went into school and acted as a class assistant (once she had her ID checked out by the local police). She started an Open University degree in education, she looked after the children and their homework, she kept the house clean and tidy and still found time to belong to an amateur dramatics club and appear in several shows a year.

No one is perfect and her slight Achilles heel was her culinary skills. She could sing like a bird on stage but her cooking did leave something to be desired. This was not a problem, but Lorry liked to leave something for Robert and me for dinner when she went off to rehearsals. One night she beamed with delight as she told us dinner was in the oven and she was off to practise for an approaching pantomime. The smell was interesting and seeping through the house from the kitchen. I turned the oven on to reheat and went to spend time with Bart and Liz before tucking them into their beds. My meal always came last in the evenings proceedings. When everyone had talked about their day, last minute homework was completed, fancy dress for the following day that had been forgotten had been sewn, children in bed – then it was time for me to sit down, relax and eat.

I opened the oven in anticipation and served the dish onto two plates. It smelt terrible. It was a special homemade 'Lorry' recipe including hot peppered smoked mackerel (ready cooked), onions and carrots – still crunchy and not cooked, garlic and white wine. After two mouthfuls it had to go and guiltily I disposed of it down the waste disposal! The following evening Lorry asked how we had enjoyed our tea – I couldn't lie and told her it was one of the worst things I had ever tasted. She wasn't bothered as in her words it had been "a bit of an experiment" but the good news was she never cooked with mackerel again!

The children were very happy with Lorraine and so were we. The summer she left us, to finish her degree, she was touring with her drama club and they were appearing down in Devon. We arranged for tickets without her knowing and arrived in time to get seated in the front row of the theatre, Bart had two model minis which went everywhere with him. He parked then neatly on the very front of the stage and waited. When the curtain went up she came onto the stage in full song. She glanced down at the minis and then to our family sitting behind them and she beamed as she sang. The kids loved the performance and they got to go backstage afterwards for a cuddle and a catch up.

Exams were fast looming for the children and I needed to make a plan. Liz was naturally quick and bright whilst Bart was bright but couldn't remember anything. I was staying away from home in Dublin, working on a three year business strategy. I mused, as I looked across St Stephen's square in the centre of Dublin, that I had no plan for my own family and their education. I was fearful that the way Bart was going he would be expelled from school aged thirteen and in a 'special school' for disruptive children. I vowed then to help Liz to pass her eleven plus so that I could afford to pay for Bart to go to a private school if the need arose.

I bought the eleven plus papers for Liz and started to introduce a bit of revision about a year before she would need to sit the exams. We would practice the questions while I cooked in the kitchen, or curled up in front of a log fire at the end of the day. Glass of wine in hand, I would sit and wait patiently while the timer ticked down the minutes. Then, when the time was up, I would find the answer book and we would check off the answers together. On more than one occasion I caused a bit of an upset when I checked her answers for a completely different test! *"The answer to 1a is 56"* I would say, *"No mum, its 12"* She would reply. We would cover 5 or 6 questions before she would ask me what set of answers I was looking at. Liz usually had the right answers- it was just me who was incapable of finding the right test in the answer book.

Despite, rather than because of, my help and coaching, Liz passed her eleven plus and was accepted into Tonbridge Grammar School for Girls. Meanwhile Bart was relatively stable but still managed to get himself into the usual amount of dodgy situations at school. His SATS exams were a few terms away and the school head of special needs – Belinda – had started the process to get Bart fully statemented for school by the local education authorities.

Initially I viewed a school statement as a bit of a stigma – something that would follow Bart into adult life, but then I just thought logically that this was something he needed at the moment to help get the best out of his education. Poor Belinda, the head of Special Needs, took thirteen hours to get the paperwork completed for his review. She told me this over a glass of wine some months later. Bart's request for being statemented went before the review board and was passed. Hurrah! He was now eligible officially for the extra support he really needed. This entitled him to one to one with a classroom assistant, who could help keep him on track during lessons.

Meanwhile at home I had bought the practise and revision books for the SATS exams. Bart was less pleased about this as it meant sitting down and concentrating, while he would rather be out having fun, but we split the time up with treats, play and study time. It was quite enlightening for me too, going over basic maths, English and science. To this day I can still recite the differences between a plant and animal cell, though I doubt Bart can or indeed when it will come in useful for me.

Chapter 15

A Close Shave for Bart

Bart was ten when he started to complain that he could feel his heart pounding in his chest. At first I just thought he was being a bit dramatic in order to get out of his studies. It never ceased to amaze me the symptoms that he could concoct to get out of his homework. But as time went on it became evident that Bart did indeed have a problem with his heart racing. It happened intermittently and because I was at work I was not around when he said it happened.

One Saturday morning Bart came racing through to the kitchen shouting "It's doing it again mummy, my hearts thumping", I sat him down and shushed him quiet whilst I put my hand against his chest. I knew he hadn't been exercising as he was in the lounge playing on his computer game – but whatever he had been doing it was not sufficient to make his heart race like this. I timed the beats for a minute and counted one hundred and sixty. I stroked his head so he didn't feel anxious, but inside I was very concerned.

The following Monday we went to the doctor's surgery. They sent us onto our local hospital where they performed an ECG which came out normal. Bart was referred to see a cardiac specialist and given a heart monitor to wear for a few days – much to his delight! His street credibility really went up at school as he had plasters stuck all over his chest and wires that fed into a recording device strapped to his waist. He looked like the bionic man and he optimised on this curiosity that bought him interest and popularity with his peers. He also got out of PE which for him was an added bonus!

Our appointment with the specialist was a few weeks later and we were directed to the children's outpatients to wait our turn. I hadn't been here since Bart was diagnosed with ADHD and little had changed. When we were called into the consultants room Bart and I were greeted by not one, but two specialists. We had the resident hospital children's cardiologist and another one from a London hospital who was doing some sort of exchange. Well on the bright side two doctors should be able to get to the bottom of things quite quickly.

First they listened to Bart's heart then they scanned him with some sort of ultrasound equipment. They asked him all the obvious questions like when did it most often occur? Had he been doing physical exercise immediately prior to an episode? I started to tell them that Bart had ADHD and was on Ritalin, but they just carried on with their procedures. They examined the test results from the ECG and heart monitor but they could find nothing. It's funny how the medical specialists used long medical words and just spoke to each other – almost as if they were speaking in a foreign tongue as if we were not present in the room.

There we sat, Bart next to me holding my hand,

whilst the two consultants muttered together, seemingly trying to outdo each other with even longer words. Most of it was going over my head and I mistakenly tried to wheedle myself into the conversation again, so I could glean some of their thoughts about Bart's diagnosis. No joy – they continued to talk at each other and ignored us completely. I reflected that this might be because they were used to dealing with children and therefore they would not normally discuss the diagnosis with them. I also conceded that some parents might not be able to understand what they were talking about and would be happy just to have a simplified précis at the end. But I wanted to be involved. The rapid heartbeat had not occurred during any of the tests on Bart, but it was very real and frightening when it happened. We needed to understand what was causing it and I needed these two rather pompous medics to get their heads from under each other's bottoms and help us.

I cleared my throat and for the third time tried to gain their attention; "He's taking Ritalin", I said in my most assertive manner. They stopped their 'medical talk' and looked directly at me and then each other. "I believe it acts like an amphetamine" I went on. Neither of them said anything, "I was thinking that if it acts like a stimulant, could it be responsible for increasing the heart rate in any way?" Now they were listening. Initially they were a bit dismissive of my theory and I may well have been clutching at straws, but something was prompting a perfectly healthy ten year old to have surges of heart beats that doubled the normal heart rate, pounded in his chest and frightened him. As his mum, I was his champion, we had fought schools, education process and procedure for the last six years and I had learnt not to give in. I had also studied Ischemic heart disease for my thesis at university and I had a fairly basic understanding that what was happening to Bart was not normal, something was causing it and could, if left unchecked, harm him or worse.

The consultants proposed to monitor him over the next few weeks and we arranged another appointment on the way out. I wasn't happy that they would identify any possible causes for Bart's palpitations but I was determined that I would do all in my power to protect him. They had conceded that his medication was amphetamine-like, but they had no other known knowledge of its affecting children in this way.

When I got home with Bart I sat and reflected. I had been mulling thoughts around my head on the drive home and counter arguing with myself. If I took Bart off his medication he would probably be expelled or excluded from school. I had experimented over the past few years by reducing his tablets and even missing some of them, but each time his behaviour and lack of concentration gave the game away and his school were quick to point out "Bart couldn't concentrate today" or "Bart was very excitable and rough in the playground today. Did he take his medication?"

No, I couldn't stop Bart's medication, but I could look for an alternative. I 'phoned CAMHS – which was the local Child and Adolescent Mental Health Services where we now went for Bart's checkups. One of the frustrating things about dealing with CAMHS at that time was lack of continuity of doctors. It seemed that each time we went we saw a different 'lay doctor' as there was a vacancy for a permanent position This meant that every time we saw a new doctor they had to be brought up to speed about Bart, his medication, his behaviour etc. We had moved on from Dr Fullers care as she tended to focus on the diagnosis of younger children and we had been told that we had to attend CAMHS because it was nearer and the next step for Bart.

I eventually got hold of the doctor who had last seen Bart at CAMHS and talked through his heart issue and our appointment with the specialists. Again I drew a blank as she said she was not aware of any side effects of his medication that could cause Bart's rapid heart rate. I realised that I needed to make a decision and told the doctor I was stopping Bart's tablets, both the day and the night medication. I couldn't prove that they were in any way responsible for Bart's problem, but intuitively as a parent I had always been suspicious of them and I was scared that if I didn't stop them, and something happened, then I would never forgive myself.

I think the doctor at CAMHS thought I was a little unhinged and over reacting. Her choice, everybody is entitled to their opinion, but he was my son, not hers. She talked about another medication that had recently come onto the UK market and said she felt that might be a suitable replacement. I was very suspicious of all psychiatric drugs – which is what these are, so I set about contacting the chemists who had carried out the research for the manufacturer in this country.

It took me ages to find a phone number for the manufacturer and when I did I had to convince 'the voice' at the other end of the 'phone that I wasn't a 'fruit cake' and I just wanted some more details on exactly how the drug worked. I was eventually put through to the research team. They explained the difference in how the two medications reacted in the brain. They told me that their product was not amphetamine based and they also told me there were no known major side effects from taking this new medication.

I felt, as a mum, that I had researched the new medication quite thoroughly, I requested papers on their research and was told that as I was not a doctor I was not permitted to receive these but they would forward them onto CAMHS and send some more 'easily digested' information for me to read. I wasn't happy about being patronised but felt that I had moved things on for Bart. I wrote to the school advising them that I had stopped Bart's medication and the reasons why. I explained that he would need to be un-medicated for about six weeks and then we would start the new regime and I asked for their patience during this process.

Interestingly Bart never had a reoccurrence of his rapid heart rate and palpitations after that. We duly returned to the specialists a few months later and they found nothing wrong with him. They wrote to me after Bart's final appointment and concluded that Bart's condition might be, in part, attributed to taking Ritalin. This was something that could not be ruled out.

It was much later on, long after Bart had stopped taking the Ritalin that I looked into any possible connections between his medication and heart problems. I Googled 'Ritalin side effects + heart' and the first item was a web site www.adrugrecall.com that quoted an American Food and Drug Administration report that said " Fifty one deaths in 2004 may have been connected to the use of ADHD medicines including Ritalin". Whilst there is not enough data to prove the drugs were responsible for the fatalities, the F.D.A. urged regulators to monitor for Ritalin heart attacks, high blood pressure and other problems.

I looked at the second web site www.ritalindeath.com. It talked about "Information for parents who are pressured to diagnose and drug their children for ADD and ADHD".

I read the heartbreaking story of a family whose son Matthew had ADHD. It says he "died suddenly on March 21st 2000. The cause of death was determined to be from long term (age seven – fourteen) use of methylphenidate, a drug commonly known as Ritalin". From this report I read "The certificate of death reads 'death caused from long term use of methylphenidate, Ritalin'". The parents went on to explain a lot of things that they had not fully understood when they had allowed their son to be prescribed the ADHD drug. I thought his saddest quote was "One toy might be recalled if one or two children die from it. How many children have to die from these drugs before we realise and put an end to this horror?"

I reflected on my hectic life style, how I was always away from home working and I thanked my lucky stars that I had always gone with my intuition. We will never know what might have happened if Bart had continued to take this medication, but I am glad I took notice when I did, sought help and made my own decisions, no matter how little substance was behind them at the time, or what people thought of me.

Chapter 16

Fun in the Sun and Goodbye to Junior School

We booked a last minute few days in Majorca at a nice quiet hotel away from the madding crowd. It was a bit of a lazy holiday where we read round the pool and swam. Constantly keeping one eye on Bart was not exactly relaxing but we were used to it, taking turns and Liz would always keep an eye out for him.

We hired a car for a couple of days and took ourselves up to the quiet North and the mountains. We explored a bay that could only be reached by a hair-raising descent on an almost single track road that zig zagged its way down the steep side of the hills. After snorkelling and an amazing paella, we made tracks for home. The road meandered across the top of the mountains and as it started its descent we saw a sign for a reservoir. Being keen ornithologists, we knew that generally water attracts birds, so we parked up, left Liz in the back of the car listening to her MP3 player and set off on foot in search of some wildlife. Naturally we couldn't leave Bart in the car as well, as it might not be there when we got back, so son in tow we climbed over a padlocked gate and followed a track towards the shimmering water in the distance.

It was mid afternoon with the sun still very high in the sky, so I tied my T- shirt round my waist and strolled on in only a swimming costume and shorts. From far away came the soft clanging of metal bells from the herd of cattle we could just about see on the other side of the reservoir. The landscape was undulating with small thorny bushes and stunted trees. We slowed in the undergrowth about twenty metres from the water's edge and I handed Bart his binoculars and told him to keep his mouth shut or he would scare away the birds.

We had picked a good spot and spent about forty minutes checking out the different bird species on the reservoir, the sound of clanging bells and cattle moving gently about. It was very peaceful. After a little while Bart started to get hot and fidgety, I was wondering if Liz was OK back in the car alone and I was desperate for a pee.

We started back towards the car, but we had walked further than we thought and I didn't think I was going to make it to the loo, so decided to take advantage of the natural local camouflage and spend a penny. Bart strolled about fifteen feet in front of me as I stooped down behind a small sparse bush. It was then that I heard a single bell, different in tone and much louder – so much nearer. It was followed by a stamping hoof and a guttural snort. I was still squatting as I heard a much louder snort and more hoof stomping. I realised what was happening and shouted to Bart who looked back over his shoulder and his face was a picture.

From my undignified position, with Rob standing next to me, I watched and listened as a large black bull trotted forward and stopped, just the other side of the bush. Mediterranean foliage tends to have no leaves, or very thin ones to stop transpiration, thus I was looking directly at one very angry bull, no more than three feet from me, with my shorts stuck around my ankles! We stayed dead still, making no sound whilst the bull gave huge snorts and continued to paw the ground. It was as if he could smell me but he couldn't see me. Bart however decided on the flight principle, he ran about four or five yards to a tree and shimmied straight up it with amazing agility. The bull seemed to focus on Bart, darted forward to the base of the tree, snorted, pawed the ground and then set off into the foliage, disappearing as quickly as he had come.

The whole episode had probably happened in only two minutes, but it seemed like a lifetime and my whole life seemed to have flashed before me. I shot up from my uncompromising position and Bart slid down the tree trunk, looking very pleased with himself and his quick reactions. His impulsivity had certainly put him out of the danger zone on this particular occasion, which is ironic because usually it exposed him to danger. We beat a very hasty retreat to the safety of the fence, looking over our shoulders as we jogged back towards the car.

By comparison, the rest of the holiday was very quiet and the only other event worthy of note was the flight back home. Over the years I had flown in and out from Gatwick on a pretty regular basis. I was usually vaguely aware of the proximity to the airport by looking out of the window. On this particular evening we had circled over Brighton and started our descent West to East. As I looked out of the window on our final descent we seemed to be approaching too fast, we had flown over

Charlwood quite high and in air time that's seconds rather than minutes to touch down. I gripped Liz's hand and whispered "we are going too fast", as I said this, the runway was underneath us, but we seemed to be too high. Almost simultaneously the flight crew pulled the nose of the plane up and aborted the landing. Gasps and shrieks filled the plane and people held onto each other as the plane climbed and banked steeply. We seemed to circle for ages after that, although it was probably only five or ten minutes at the most. The landing, when it came, was fast, steep and bumpy. The passengers let out long sighs and applause as we taxied back to the terminal. The only person who looked relaxed was Bart who was perfectly calm. I should have realised then that he would want to fly one day.

Back to school and Bart was fast approaching his SATS and we cranked up the revision at home. It didn't all have to be done sitting at a table. On one Sunday, when our friend Tony was staying, we went to Hampton Court for an outing and used the time in the car on the way to revise reproduction. Bart was completely cool about this but Tony spent most of the journey blushing!

Bart was predicted to get two threes and a four for his SATS, but by working through the syllabus together in bite size chunks, when he finally took them, he actually got two five's and a four. His teachers and we were delighted. He had exceeded their expectations and it made him and me feel very good.

We had a meeting with the educational psychologist

before he left his junior school. She was the lady who had first assessed Bart at the age of five. Bart entered the room, was polite, answered the questions fluently and honestly and I was dead proud of him. After he left the room, we summed up the meeting and she looked across the table at me, one eye brow arched, "Who would have believed it?" she asked. She said she was amazed with Bart, his achievements and behaviour and acknowledged that we, as parents, had done a remarkable job. I could have kissed her! It was so rare to get any compliments, just complaints usually. We had come on quite a journey since our first meeting, when she had told me Bart was too young to be told he 'hurt my heart' when he did things wrong. I still stand by that opinion; if he was old enough to perform an action, he was old enough to consider the implications and consequences – how would he learn otherwise?

During his final year at junior school Bart had grown an incredible nine inches in just the ten months and this coincided with him stopping taking the Ritalin. It may have been a coincidental growth spurt, but he had always been small, thin and rather "elfin" like for his age, now he was tall and skinny, which earned him the nickname 'Bean', that and his uncanny ability to pull a perfect 'Mr Bean' smile, thumbs up, bottom lip rolled out and eyes wide open!

Chapter 17

Bart's Birthday Bow

Bart's eleventh birthday was that May and his passion for archery was growing. So what do you buy a boy with ADHD, who has the attention span of a gnat and is highly impulsive? Why a professional bow and arrows of course!

We had bought him a basic long bow and arrows the previous Christmas and, convinced that this would be a five minute wonder, we had taken him that Spring to an archery club nearby to see if he had any talent or would concentrate for long enough to get the arrow in the bow before he got bored! The thing about Bart was that he could get immensely interested in something and then tire of it very quickly. I didn't want to buy a load of expensive gear that would end up on ebay six months later, so we bought the basic bow to see how he got along. We set up a small make shift target in the garden and always supervised him when he was shooting. It became clear that Bart had quite a natural skill and managed to hit the target far more frequently than the rest of the family put together. At the archery club Bart was regarded as a bit of a natural and some of the club members thought he might be quite successful at the sport.

This praise was good for Bart's self esteem. It was difficult to build Bart's self confidence as he had received so much criticism and verbal knock backs in life. The usual and expected negative comments continually reinforced in Bart's mind that he was useless. There is only so much praise the family can give before he worked out that "you are my mum so you would say that" started to creep into the conversation

After a six month wait Bart was accepted for "trial" into the archery club. It quickly became clear that the basic bow I had purchased was not good enough and the club kindly lent him a better bow for the first few sessions. On Bart's birthday we decided he had shown sufficient commitment to the sport and we bought his first proper bow.

I found a shop that specialised in all the different types of bows and equipment. We purchased a medium priced beginners bow – which still seemed very expensive to me – and all the other ancillary pieces of equipment including a couple of boxes of arrows and the largest straw target butt that they sold. We live in the country with no direct neighbours and I was fairly sure that we could create a decent range for target practice.

When Bart unwrapped his new bow, on his birthday, he was as happy as a pig in muck and it was straight out into the garden to practice. We heaved the six foot round butt up onto its easel and went through the ground rules that we had learnt at the club, arrow out of bow at all times and pointing to the floor pre-firing, no arrows straight up into the sky and on no occasion aim for the cat! They hadn't taught us the rule about the cat but I included it just in case.....

Bart really enjoyed his sessions at the archery club each Sunday morning. Before he fired a bow they went through the safety and handling aspects. They were very strict and whistles were blown when firing could commence and when it had to stop. Bart respected the discipline and rules because it was clear and done for a reason which he understood. I will admit that I spoke quietly to the club secretary about Bart's ADHD before he joined, but any misgivings they may have had soon gave way to admiration when they saw him shoot.

One of the first competitions Bart took part in was the club clout. Basically it involved a series of rope circles on the ground several different distances away from the archers, each marked with a flag. Instead of the usual archery position, the competitor raised their bows up towards the sky and fired arrows up in an ark, rather like a shooting star. The winner was the one to get closest to the flag in the centre of the rope ring, but from the position you fired in it was impossible to judge where your arrows landed. I had the slight disadvantage of being very short sighted so I wasn't much help to Bart either. Bart loved this competition as it gave him a legitimate reason to fire arrows up into the air – every ADHD boys dream! He seemed to instinctively understand the trajectory needed and amazingly he scored well in this competition, consistently putting his arrows near the flags.

The club members were made up of a wide mixture of individuals from young wealthy professionals, some of whom had all the gear but not much skill, to older retired people who treated the sport rather like I imagined it would be in a bowls club, leisurely, skilful and with an undercurrent of politics and protocol that we never did fully understand.

Despite Bart's rather energetic presence and his ability to say something just at the wrong time, he was well accepted in the club and tolerated by all. One guy, Michael, took a particular interest in Bart. He recognised his raw talent and helped him with his technique and his equipment. He also gave him little gifts like a quiver to put his arrows in and a big wool tassel to dry his arrows.

Michael also encouraged Bart to enter competitions. At first Bart was really reluctant. I think he was scared of failure and because his self esteem was low, he didn't want to risk failing in a sport that he enjoyed. He needn't have worried though. Every competition he entered he either won gold or silver. He was the county champion within his age group within months of taking the sport up. I tried to motivate him to think about the Olympics but his response was that there were much better archers than him. Because he found it easy, he didn't see his achievements as special. He never told anybody about the competitions he won – let alone bragged about them and it was almost as if he undervalued them because he had a natural talent. Bart had achieved in this sport and, unlike most who would continue to progress and advance, he gradually grew bored with it and 'retired' by the time he was thirteen. I felt excited and proud for Bart that, for once in his life he was best at something, but he would just shrug it off as if anyone could have done it.

Chapter 18

Secondary Education – But Which School?

We needed to make a choice for Bart's secondary school and this bought its own issues to the family. Most of Bart's friends were going to the local high school and this would have been the logical step as it was the nearest secondary school to home. However during my time with the ADHD support group I had come across several parents who had bad experiences with the school. They had each been seen individually and it had been suggested to them that their son/daughter was the only child in the year with ADHD, they were falling behind and might it be a good idea to think about moving onto another school where they may get along better?

It was just a peculiar turn of fate that these three parents belonged to our ADHD support group and attended the monthly meeting at my house, just a week after they had been seen by the school. The insinuation by the school that they were the only parents with a disruptive child was divisive and clearly untrue, but this was the practice in some schools. Coping with too many special needs children exerts a great strain on the school's resources, unless the correct statement is in place with additional help which is budgeted for. This school seemed to take the view that it was easier to 'squeeze out' the disruptive element, making the classes easier to manage and less resource hungry.

Whilst Bart had his sights firmly set on the local school, I was looking elsewhere. I visited another school that was a further five miles from home. The school was much smaller, with only eight hundred pupils as opposed to over two thousand pupils at the nearer school. They also had over twelve per cent special needs students, with varying needs, so they were clearly able to cope with individuals. I went and met the head of special needs, Walter, and talked to him about my son. Even on that first meeting I got a good feeling about him and his integrity. He walked me round the school, whilst outlining his philosophy and the schools' ethos. I liked him. I liked what he said and I felt sure that Bart would fare far better in a school where he had a name, rather than one of the two thousand, but Bart didn't actually see it that way.....

I got dates thorough for open evenings for three schools and we did the rounds, turning up, listening, wandering round and desperately trying to make the right decision that would serve Bart best. The school I favoured, De Leeds, was probably the most run down and ill equipped school with the poorest Ofsted report. It was located in a less affluent area and the catchment area was very mixed, but I felt their culture and approach was the best.

Bart came with Robert and me for the first year talk. I had raced home from London on a slightly earlier train and put my horse to bed in her stable. Wearing a pale linen suit and high heels I was now sitting in the school hall quietly examining a small piece of something unpleasant on my shoe and savouring the thought of a glass of wine. We had arrived part way through the principal's speech and it was only minutes before he finished and a very young and energetic deputy head stood to speak.

He gave a motivational speech about his reason for being at the school, the fact that he originally attended De Leeds as a pupil, left with no formal qualifications, went to America to pursue a football career and returned to the UK when forced to retire due to injury. He had then completed teacher training and taken up a position in his old school because he wanted to give something back. Splendid, I thought, a man with a social conscience. Bart sat next to me looking bored and fidgeting.

When the speeches were over we were invited to find members of staff to chat to about our children. I was dead keen to meet the deputy head – along with most of the other parents and we queued quietly until nearly 9 pm before finally gaining an audience with him. As I started to speak he asked me to confirm what year Bart was in. I told him that we were prospective parents, to which he informed us that we had come to the year seven parents meeting and could we come back again next week as that was the correct date! Hell's teeth, all that rushing. I had been out of the house since 6 am that morning and we had the wrong night!

Exhausted, I walked across the car park and spent several minutes thinking the central locking had gone on my car before realizing I was trying to get into someone else's car. I found ours and trundled towards home with Bart going on about hating the school, Robert going on about why couldn't I get the right date, and me wondering what, if anything, there was in the fridge for tea.

The evening was finished off perfectly when having returned home, I walked through the hall to find a live slow worm slithering along with 3 cats hot on its tail. I have a complete phobia about reptiles in general and snakes in particular. Although not a snake, it was the same dimension, moved like one and pressed all my panic buttons. I yelped as I nearly trod on it and it writhed along the mat, the cats sprang into action and Bart flew onto the scene. He flung open the front door and fended off the cats simultaneously. Robert and he ushered it out and I watched it slither off into one of my flower beds. What a perfect day I thought as the tip of its tail disappeared. Bad day at the office, worse evening and an unwanted gift bought in by the cats. Too tired to eat I retired to bed.

The following week was déjà vu but this time we left Bart at home with the nanny. We sat through another set of speeches, sprinted to be second in line for a chat with the deputy head and then whizzed round the uniform sale in next to no time. Clutching carrier bags we returned home laughing at the previous week's events. But on opening the back door it was clear that all was not well. All the house lights were off and there was the sound of soft sobbing coming from the downstairs nannies bedroom. Bart was nowhere to be seen and one of the kitchen walls was covered in, what looked like Bart's dinner.

I had an unpleasant feeling of doom as I mounted the stairs, two at a time, and rushed along the landing to Bart's bedroom. The door was closed and locked from the inside and he wasn't coming out. The good news was I could hear him speaking so I knew he was at least alive. I raced back down to the nannies' room, knocked on her door and asked her what had happened. Petra was a temporary nanny and had only been with the family a matter of weeks. From what I could gather Bart had come home from school in a bad mood. This had continued on into the evening. He had refused to eat his dinner and after some sort of exchange, his dinner ended up on a wall and Bart had stormed off upstairs. After picking up the broken plate, Petra said she had gone in search of Bart and was alarmed to find him lying across one of the oak timber beams in the ceiling with a dressing gown cord wrapped round his neck, threatening to jump if he had to go to De Leeds School!

I calmed Petra down and then returned to Bart's room. I sat on one side of the door, calmly negotiating its opening, whilst reflecting that while I was at school buying his uniform, Bart was so unhappy about the choice of school that he had put himself in a very dangerous position.

Eventually he opened the door, flung himself into my arms and we both had a good cry. I stroked his head and stayed with him until he fell asleep – I knew better than to start the "what did you do that for?" or "why didn't you tell me how you were feeling?" debate there and then. Bart was emotionally exhausted, I wasn't far behind and I would pick my time to talk through the evening's events when we were in a calm zone. Meanwhile I ran my fingers through his hair until he fell fast asleep, before taking myself to bed and waiting for sleep to come and repair me. After several long and reasoned debates with Bart we settled on De Leeds as our first choice of school for Bart's secondary education.

Chapter 19

A Wild Time in Africa and the Usual Family Crisis

That summer I had planned a trip to South Africa for the family. I had been lucky enough to go there on business the previous year and although it had only been a four day trip, the country and its people had left a lasting impression and I wanted my family to share in that. We flew overnight to Johannesburg and were met at the airport by a girlfriend of mine who had arranged for a hire car and booked us into a local hotel. On my previous trip I had taken a small overnight bag and a very large suitcase filled with gifts for a local school. Pens, paper, chocolate and unwanted exercise books from Bart's school that had been printed with the margin on the wrong side of the page, so they were just using them as scrap. My 'gifts' had gone to a school on the outskirts of Johannesburg where children lived in poverty, families were plagued with AIDS and an exercise book was a luxury – even if the margin was in the wrong place.

I had arranged to take the family to visit the school because I wanted Liz and Bart to see the real world, what hardships these children endured and yet still they managed to radiate happiness with their beautiful smiles. We pulled up in front of the school, a two storey concrete building with no glass in the windows and a baked red earth surrounding instead of the manicured grass and playgrounds that we were used to at home. The whole of the side of the reception building had a brightly coloured school motto painted on it, but instead of the usual Latin phrase, which roughly translated meant something like 'work hard and you will conquer' this mural simply said "wear a condom, sex spreads AIDS which kills". This stark message was the first indicator for my kids that school life here was very different from school life at home, with all the comforts that we take so much for granted.

We had coffee with the headmaster and he explained to us about his school, the age range of the children and how different it was to my own children's experiences. Then he took us for a walk around the school as he was obviously very proud. The play area was just red dusty earth and here and there were posts stuck into the ground that marked out the football and volleyball pitches. Around the edge of the 'playing field' were a host of tiny strips of land that had been cultivated with vegetables. The head explained that in this region over twenty per cent of the population had AIDS. Many of the parents of the children were too ill to work and had no means of earning a wage to buy food, so the school encouraged them to grow food for their families on these tiny allotments. I could see Liz and Bart mentally comparing their own schools as they took in the facts about the school and its pupils.

The head teacher then took us to some of the

classrooms and we met teachers and children who greeted us with bright warm smiles and some sad, wary eyes. We chatted to them about what they were learning and when it was time go the class erupted into song, with their beautiful rich voices and sense of harmony.

It was an unusual way to start a holiday, but it gave us a greater understanding of the people and the hardships they faced in comparison to our own lives. As I smiled and listened to the song, my eyes filled with tears of compassion. I thought about my own plight, working full time, constantly juggling my time between home and work, Bart's special needs – and I decided that by comparison, my life was pretty straight forward.

We set off the following day towards the Kruger National Park. It was a long drive and I had booked an overnight stay in Cyberlee Lodge, a small hotel that had individual guest bungalows and three large boxer dogs that wandered in and out of each one and settled where they could get the most attention. We even had our own small swimming pool at the back which, though not heated, was refreshing after the long days drive and a great place for Bart and Liz to let off steam.

That evening we went over to the main house for dinner and the food was delicious. Returning to our bungalow we found that the fire had been lit in the living room and the dogs had settled in front of it for the night. We talked about the stark contrast between the visit to the school and the place we were staying in and acknowledged how privileged we were. I would have loved to have stayed there a week, but it was the most expensive accommodation of the holiday and intended as a treat to unwind after the past few hectic months, the flight over and before our trip to the Kruger – where our accommodation promised to be a lot more basic.

The following morning we had a lazy breakfast outside, shaded by the huge trees that towered above us and we watched the monkeys swinging about in the canopy. One ventured down to a table nearby and ran off with a sugar bowl, which he carried up the tree and then proceeded to throw sugar cubes down on the residents below. The bowl followed shortly after, much to Liz and Bart's delight!

From the tranquillity of Cyberlee we drove on towards the Kruger and after a few hours Robert started to complain of stomach pains. The pain continued to increase so we made a detour to a town as we didn't want to be stuck in the National park if it was something serious. By this point he was doubled up with pain, running a fever and feeling very sick. Though not the right area or season, Robert seemed to be displaying most of the symptoms for malaria. What a good start to the holiday!

We found a local clinic and waited around for a couple of hours until the doctor was available. He announced that Robert had a urinary infection and he gave us three sets of pills, yellow, red and blue, which looked suspiciously like smarties! But, tablets on board we set off again for the Kruger and managed to arrive just half an hour before they shut the gates for the night.

We had two small self-contained, round huts. I had asked for them to be adjoining but they weren't so we solved that problem by dragging the mattress into one of them so that we could be together. "It's like posh camping" I announced to the kids and mentally checked out which bed I would sleep in – there was no way I would be the one sleeping on the mattress on the floor.

Each hut had a tiny kitchen and a barbecue just outside, so we popped to get some food and I set about making a salad, watched closely by a lizard on the wall, Robert went to lie down for a while and Bart started the barbecue. As dusk turned to dark we could hear the roar of lions as they visited the water hole just outside our camp.

Robert seemed to be getting progressively worse and the barbecue wouldn't light. Bart ever resourceful disappeared and returned with some kindling which looked remarkably like reeds. The barbecue took its time to get going and he made several missions to procure more kindling. At one point when he had disappeared, I heard loud German voices and Bart returned with another handful of reeds. He said that he had told the German family that it was a real lion they could hear roaring and that the guy had laughed at him and told him it wasn't. I told Bart not to worry and could he just stay still long enough to get the barbecue going, then we could all eat and go to bed?

Robert was groaning so I went in to check on him and noticed that our thatched roof looked remarkably like what we had used to get the barbecue going. "Bart, have you been stripping our roof to start the barbecue?" I asked. "No, its all right Mum, I've been stealing the German's roof" was his reply. He then elaborated on his technique of popping over to their hut for a chat, then sneaking round the back and pulling some of their roof reeds out! I told Bart off, made a mental note to stop

Robert doing his silly German impersonations of "don't mention the war" and carried on cooking. I think we finally ate at about 11 pm, by which time everybody, including the lions and the Germans had long since feasted and retired to bed!

We were woken at 4.30 the following morning by the jangle of my mobile alarm. Robert seemed to be quite rested, the kids were still half asleep and I hadn't slept a wink. I was over tired, worried about Robert and thinking about all kinds of things in the early hours of the morning, when even the smallest things can get blown out of all proportion.

We had booked an early morning jeep safari which left the compound at 5 am, before the sun came up. Bart clambered up onto the jeep which was more like a bus, and had been specially modified with rows of seats that were higher towards the rear of the vehicle. He plumped for the back seat and we all followed. We had only driven five hundred yards from the compound gates when we spotted a lioness and her two cubs. Dawn was only just breaking and the sun would not be up for at least another hour. As daylight came, we all snapped our cameras happily and the sights of the elephant, giraffe and rhinos' were stunning. We were totally absorbed with the wildlife and bird life and it was only on the way back to the camp that I started to shiver. Sitting at the back of the vehicle meant we were highest for great views but also most exposed as the cold morning air rushed past us. I had been so enthralled with what I could see that I hadn't realised I had become extremely cold. When it became clear that the shivering was getting worse, not better, the driver passed back some blankets and the family tucked me up in them. I must admit I was pleased to get back to our hut, where it took several minutes under a hot shower before I started to feel warm again, only I could almost go down with hypothermia on an African safari!

We loved our time in the Kruger. We would set out in the car and take hours to drive just nineteen miles. For once Bart seemed quite content to sit in the car and watch.

Robert was still not feeling too good the following day so I drove the family on a little route I had planned. The first part was fairly uneventful, we saw more zebra, kudu and elephants and all was going well when I decided to go off the main tarmac road and take some of the dirt roads – more off the beaten track and away from other vehicles. We had more fun off road, even if the car wasn't really designed for it and it was more exciting for the kids. I had just come round a narrow bend where the road opened up and in front of us was a coach that had stopped – which was a surprise really as this was one of the few vehicles we saw off the main road. I stopped about fifteen yards behind the coach and it was clear that there was an attraction on the left of us as all the people at the back of the coach were looking that way. And indeed there was a large group of elephant with their young. As my family looked to the left, I turned my head to the right – just as a large bull elephant stomped out of the undergrowth, trunk raised. He could see his family across the dirt track, but the coach was between him and them and this had put the elephant in a bit of a bad mood. I caught the family's attention as I said "oh sh*t", their heads spun to the right and they immediately saw my concern.

The next bit all seemed to happen in slow motion. The bull elephant started to stomp the ground, he lifted his head, called and got ready to charge. The people in the coach carried on looking to the left, oblivious to his presence. I desperately tried to find reverse gear. The elephant started to charge the coach. The people on the coach started to panic with arms and cameras flying everywhere. The elephant charged the coach just as its driver set off very swiftly, with passengers losing their balance and toppling over in the aisle. I eventually found reverse and the car shot backwards – completely unaware or bothered if anything was behind me – which luckily it wasn't The elephant raised his trunk at the fast disappearing coach, in what might be construed as a single finger salute and I just sat there shaking. The elephant then strolled over to his family and Robert, white faced, suggested he took over the driving from then.

From the Kruger we made our way back to Johannesburg and flew to Victoria Falls in Zimbabwe. We had been advised to say we were living in South Africa as the hotel we had booked was already very expensive and apparently British tourists paid double. Unsure as to whether this was in fact true, we decided to go along with the plan and we signed in with a fictitious address in Johannesburg. We stayed three nights and on the first day we found a local guide to take us on the famous walk along past all the different falls.

Bart was intent on climbing and swinging from trees and I apologised to Gracious, our guide, but he was very relaxed about his job and he showed affection to Bart. Perhaps the children of his other clients were a little more restrained and demure. I kept a close eye and hand on Bart for some parts of the walk, where we got very close to the edge of the gorge, but Gracious seemed to have a way with Bart and Bart respected this gentle six foot giant of a man. We were so taken by Gracious and the story of his family that we sent him a £20 tip wrapped in foil and a letter of thanks on our return to the UK. I had been told that tin foil apparently stops interception of money by X-ray, I am not sure this is true but I have often wondered if he ever got our letter, even then the country was in serious turmoil and people's lives were being changed forever.

On our final day in Zimbabwe we organised a very early start to take a trip into Botswana for a river and land safari in the Chobe National Park. There were only eight of us on the trip and we crossed the border into Botswana observed by a warthog that looked remarkably like Pumba from The Lion King.

When we arrived at the river for the 'cruise' I was not entirely surprised to see that there was no boat, just some oil cans ingeniously bound together with ropes and boards on top to form a platform. My suspicions of its stability, or lack of it, were confirmed when our guide asked us to remain seated at all times and not to all move to one side of the craft if we saw something as it would capsize! There was a small outboard motor at one end, about a dozen assorted plastic chairs along the sides and a cool box with soft drinks at the front. Despite its basic appearance, the raft did in fact float and we had an amazing trip round the reed beds watching monitor lizards and crocodiles basking in the sun with still, unblinking eyes.

I went through the usual "don't get near the edge Bart, and whatever you do, don't fall in" speech, which was just as well, as the river hosted many creatures, large and small, and occasionally a hippo would suddenly appear on the surface from its submerged watery rest. The river was very wide in places and there was only one dodgy incident, when we were near to the river bank and clearly aggravating a bull elephant who was calling to his heard across the river. His size was formidable and his attitude soon persuaded the guides to back off a little. We were rewarded when the whole herd crossed the river in front of us. The adults swam across, keeping the baby elephants in their midst, with their tiny trunks pointing to the sky.

On the final morning of our holiday, Robert went to get the bill whilst the children and I enjoyed our last swim in the pool. He returned a bit red faced with the bill and we had a frantic thirty minutes counting out the sterling and dollars we had between us. We just about scraped the cash up to pay the bill as well as ensuring we had $20 each to pay as an exit fee at the airport. Of course we could have used our credit cards if we hadn't said we were from South Africa!!

Chapter 20

Bart's New Friends

With the end of the summer, the children returned to school and Bart started at De Leeds. His first day was good and bad. Good for Bart as it was very short and bad for me. Having taken time off especially from work, we drove up to school with a last minute pep talk on first appearances only to find the school deserted. I had in fact got the wrong date and school didn't start for three more days. One might have thought I would learn from this but in truth I took Bart to school on the first day of the autumn term for the next few years and only once did I get the right date.

Bart got off to quite a good start at De Leeds. ADHD kids often don't cope well with a change of routine, but considering he didn't know a soul at the school, he settled in and started to make friends. He was now a small fish in a big pool and I think the shock of this helped to check his behaviour a bit. He became steadier and certainly, for the first few months, things were very quiet on the home/school communication front.

I am not sure why they say opposites attract, that was certainly not the case with Bart when he brought friends home. Bart seemed to attract friends, particularly boys, who were exactly the same as him – like peas out of a pod. One of his best school friends proudly announced he had ADHD within twenty minutes of his first visit to the house. In one respect this was fine, as having managed Bart all these years I was more than a match for any of his friends. On the other hand it made the task of parental supervision twice as difficult as the two of them could literally get into double trouble and they would disappear from the garden the moment you turned your back.

Our garden rises up a hill and backs onto woodland. Bart and friends could play for hours up there, making camps, lighting fires and cooking bacon and beans in an old frying pan. Rather than stop them making a fire, I'd show them how to do it safely, working on the theory that kids are going to push the boundaries anyway and it's better to embrace this challenge and teach them, rather than waiting for the accident to happen. I didn't obviously know that over the next few months they would experiment by igniting pressurised cans and attempt to make different forms of incendiary devices from gas lighters!

As Bart grew older he demanded more freedom and he and his best friend Sid would set off over the fields to find new adventures, with the customary "now don't get into any trouble you two" from me, which generally didn't make a blind bit of difference. Either the local neighbours were very tolerant or they didn't know where he lived to come and complain!

On one occasion Sid and Bart arrived back home, just as it was getting dark. I took one look at them romping up the garden and shouted "stay outside!" Both boys were absolutely covered from head to foot in thick black stinking mud. All I could see were two pairs of eyes and it was a job to work out which one was Bart until he spoke. The stench from the mud was disgusting, so I made them stand on the lawn and jet hosed the pair of them down. The mud was clay and it stuck to their clothes, so I made them strip off to underwear before allowing them indoors for a bath. I spent the next half hour jet hosing their clothes on the lawn. A casual inquiry as to their whereabouts told me they had been in a neighbour's grounds and more specifically in their lake which consisted of about one foot of water and two feet of mud. I went through the usual "What would have happened to you if you had got stuck?" and they sheepishly responded that they had got stuck and had to rescue each other on their bellies. A likely story, but after three separate machine washes, most of the mud came out of their clothes and what didn't come clean got thrown away.

Bart's first year at De Leeds was generally quite good for me too. Parent's evening was a bit of a revelation when a teacher disclosed that Bart had been up to his tricks of playing the fool in his German lessons. They had been asked to make Easter cards, but Bart had decided he could make better use of his time making a German soldier model and parachute. Apparently Bart launched the parachute on its maiden flight, just as the teacher was in full flow. At parents evening the teacher reminded Bart of this incident and that this type of behaviour was not acceptable in his class. I watched as Bart squirmed in his seat, then with a twinkle in his eye, the teacher turned to us and said it was a fine piece of engineering that flew well! A teacher with a sense of humour who was not petty enough to make an example of Bart, he made his point and complemented Bart at the same time. Respect is a two way process. Adults often take the approach that because they are in authority they automatically command respect, but in fact if you can show a child some respect or humour you will gain far more loyalty and respect much quicker.

Chapter 21

A Glimmer of Hope

Being a full time working mother has its advantages and disadvantages. On one down side you don't see as much of your children as you would like. You miss important milestones like the first steps or words, or the school nativity and I carried an eternal guilt that I wasn't around enough. This meant that all of my home time was dedicated to the children and my poor husband was relegated to the bottom of the need stakes. But on the positive side I approached motherhood as a well rounded individual, with many of life's lessons learnt the hard way. Because time spent with the children was limited, it made it very precious and spurred me on to do all sorts of escapades that I may not have had the money or time to do, had I been at home with them all day. One of these treats was family holidays.

After Bart's first term at his new school I booked a very last minute holiday to Jordan. By now Liz had a complete phobia of flying so I tried to break the news gently that we would not be travelling there by car! At that time there was considerable unrest in the Middle East and I checked the British Government web site that advised travellers not to holiday there, but the tickets were bought, we had the visas and the tour operators informed us that Jordan was quite quiet at the moment. We flew late in the evening and landed, their time, about 1.30 the following morning. Although autumn, the heat blasted us as we stepped off the plane. Our travel guide met us and we were driven through Amman as he explained the fact that it was Ramadan, suggested appropriate dress and said that from his perspective there was little or no danger from terrorist activity. We might not be able to get an alcoholic drink but at least we would be safe.

After a fitful and very hot night's sleep we set off to view the ruins at Amman before driving onto the dead sea for a swim – or rather a float. Bart went off to change into his swimmers with his dad and I shouted words of warning into the men's changing room about the fact that *"you can't really swim in the Dead Sea"*, *"the salt and mineral concentration burns so don't get it into your eyes"*, and *"don't splash the other bathers or you won't be too popular!"* Liz and I exited from the changing rooms in our swimmers just in time to see Bart haring down the beach and straight into the water. When he was up to his knees he just flopped down into the water, screeched and ran out to find a shower to get the salt out of his eyes. Kids..... Sometimes you just can't tell them! Once Bart and the rest of us had got used to the concept that about fifty per cent of your body mass remains on top of the water we had great fun and there was only one point when I spotted Bart on the horizon and wondered if he planned to scull to Israel and cause a political incident, but Bart was getting much better at responding to requests and instructions – rather like a dog – and he soon made for shore when I mentioned food and drink.

The people on the trip were a great eclectic bunch of individuals from all walks of life. We had a retired military doctor and his wife, a couple of nurses who had left their children behind with family at home and had just come for the sun and the fun, a marine biologist and his wife who was an A&E nurse in New Zealand and a lovely elderly couple who were in their eighties!

Clearly we had good medical expertise should it be needed. Bart always related better to adults than people of his own age. When booking the holiday we were given the choice to go with the children's tour or the adults, but Bart preferred to hang out with the adults which was fine by me as it meant he kept out of trouble most of the time. Because there were only about fourteen of us on the trip we travelled in a tiny coach, and the only form of air conditioning was to open the windows. The elderly couple were seasoned travellers and Hazel, the wife, had brought crosswords that she had cut out of the Times to test our mental agility on the long, dusty roads between stops.

On the second night the bus pulled into Petra and we stayed in a hotel right by the local mosque. Our rooms were right next door to the minaret tower so both mornings we got an early alarm call as the worshippers were called to prayer around 4 am.

The ancient city of Petra was truly breathtaking. We set off on foot from the hotel and Liz and I opted to ride Arab horses down to the main entrance that leads to the 'lost city'. The entrance to the site is through a long sandstone gorge that twists and winds its way for about half a mile. Having watched all of the Indiana Jones movies we walked down the gorge humming the theme music, chatting and taking pictures of the fantastic rock structure that had been carved by wind and water over the years.

When the gorge finally reaches the site it opens out modestly onto the Treasury, which is the famous building often featured in magazines and publications. The sheer size of the building and the fact that it has actually been carved out of the stone is amazing. We sat in the shade and marvelled at the ornate carvings of pillars and figures and the tiny footholds that go up the face of the rock on either side acting as ladders. Our guide took us further down the valley and showed us round many other carved buildings some fifty feet above the ground level. The climbs up to these houses were quite steep and potentially dangerous, if you didn't look where you were going, but that didn't faze Bart, who jumped from rock to rock like a gazelle.

Being with a mixed group meant that some people needed a helping hand for the climbs and I realised that Bart was actually helping them. Although his impulsivity and hyperactivity could be a nightmare, Bart had somehow won the hearts of this group of people and their initial looks of concern that a 'boy' was on the holiday had faded into pleasure at sharing his company.

After a long leisurely lunch in the shade we elected to climb the eight hundred odd steps up to the Monastery. You could hire a donkey for the trip but I needed the exercise and I secretly thought it might be a great way to wear Bart out. Stupid really as Bart, with his 'batteries', never seemed to wear out. The climb was long and there was one part where a path clung to the rock face and there was a sheer drop off to the left. I held the wall and Liz's hand and insisted Bart hold his father's hand, but of course he wouldn't and I watched, heart in throat as he bounded fearlessly forward, glancing over the edge, whilst Liz and I stumbled along, knees knocking and clinging to the rock wall.

The view from the top was panoramic. We had to clamber over a few boulders and follow a rough path, but we sat on the rocks and looked down and across almost to the end of the world. In Bart's favour, he was incredibly sure footed and despite my own personal fear for his safety, he did behave in a mature way. I have never believed in stopping my children doing something because of my own personal fear. Sometimes it is very hard to give them the rules and stand back, but trust breeds responsibility and looking back I realise that some of the escapades on our holidays allowed Bart to develop his own sense of personal respect for people and dangerous situations.

The path down from the Monastery was just as arduous as the path up and I was personally delighted when we met a small local boy who offered to rent us some donkeys for the final part of the descent back to the Treasury. I am afraid we all misbehaved a bit on that ride. The donkeys were eager to go home and we had all seen the scene from Indiana Jones where Indiana and his dad charge along on their ponies. So with a quick "Ye Ha" we nudged the donkeys into canter and tore up the central 'road' singing "Der der der der – Der

der derh", the theme music from the film! We got a few disapproving looks from some of the tourists but most of them stood back smiling and we certainly were a success with the local boys who seemed most amused by these 'mad tourists'.

That evening we heard there was a local Turkish bath and massage close by the hotel. Bart rushed round to the rest of our group and enticed all but the very faint hearted to come with us. It was a hilarious experience as we bobbed between cold showers and the excessively hot steam rooms waiting our turn to be lathered and scrubbed, then massaged to within an inch of our lives. There was some sort of queuing system, but it was a bit chaotic and other locals just kept getting in front of us. Eager not to miss our turn, I returned to the dark steam room and shouted across to Robert to get a wiggle on and come out. He didn't respond and it was very misty in there so I popped my head back in and barked at him in a very loud voice. I must admit to being quite embarrassed when a complete stranger walked out and looked questioningly at me. Bart and Robert were already having their hose down and poor, long suffering Liz just stood next to me and turned bright red as I apologised profusely!

That evening we met up with the other children's tour operated by our travel company. I was sitting quietly with Bart writing his travel diary when I heard a really obnoxious Englishman's' voice order the waiter to bring his finest wine. His voice was rough and his manner condescending. It was one of those scenarios when you feel embarrassed to be and associated with that sort of behaviour. The rest of our group appeared for dinner and the loud mouth continued to make rude and condescending comments to the waiters.

Our group were usually quite chatty and noisy over meals but this guy's attitude sucked and we were all a bit subdued. The other group were still at the table when Liz got up to get her main course, embarrassed and self conscious her chair fell back and clanged to the floor. The guy with the big mouth didn't miss an opportunity to heckle and shout something rude across the restaurant and suddenly it was bedlam. Our group rose and started shouting at the other table, the guy got up and postulated looking for a fight and to my complete surprise our marine biologist jumped up and made his way over to their table. He stood towering over the loud mouth and as he was around eight inches taller he looked down into the guy's eyes and asked him if he wanted to take things further? Luckily the loud mouth had the sense to back down, apologised for his behaviour and he and his party skulked out of the restaurant.

Liz was still bright red but the rest of our group smiled and settled back down. The very relieved waiters gave us wine on the house and our two tour guides admitted that the man was a loud mouthed nightmare and it was better for us to have sorted out the situation than the locals – which was the way it looked as if it was going.

From then on our group was truly bonded. The next morning we set off for Little Petra a few miles away. Again the site is approached between rocks which gradually come together to a narrow gorge. The plan was to climb the last bit of the gorge, pass through a very narrow crevice and, have mint tea overlooking the spectacular view on the other side. The two nurses amongst us were larger than life in size and sense of humour, but neither of them had a head for heights and you could always hear from some distance away when they were performing a task they didn't like. On this occasion one of them was almost literally stuck near the top of the gorge. She was squealing with fright and laughing at the same time. She couldn't go forward and didn't want to go backwards. Bart was determined to help her and gave her an almighty push on her bum to move her on. When they got to the top he guided her down the final ten feet onto a stone platform that bizarrely served as a makeshift tea shop and had the most amazing view. I thought she might have been offended at Bart manhandling her, but she was just very grateful that he had spurred her on to make the effort to get there – the view after all was breathtaking. She had boys of her own of a similar age at home and she just adopted Bart after that, any dodgy situations and she would call for him.

On the penultimate night we slept in the desert at Wadi Rum. Earlier in the day we went in jeeps to discover ancient carvings and places where Lawrence of Arabia was said to have been. We had all walked up a steep sand dune and then rolled down it whilst those below took photographs. It was an amazing feeling of freedom and it wasn't until afterwards that one of the guides told us that recently a local boy had been bitten by a snake doing the very same thing! Sometimes a little knowledge is a dangerous thing and no knowledge at all is even better!

We all climbed fifty feet onto a rock ledge and our guides made a fire, brewed mint tea and we watched the huge sun sink behind the rocks. Afterwards, we returned to camp, which consisted of a long Bedouin tent open on one side, with smaller more modern tents with zip and mattresses behind. We had the most amazing evening round the campfire. The food was delicious and although it was Ramadan, there were beers and other sorts of local drinks. I think Robert must have tried everything because at one point in the evening I was vaguely aware that he was dancing round the fire with the Arab men!

When finally it was bedtime, people started to move off to the comfort of the tents behind the Bedouin camp. Bart and Liz were desperate to sleep under the stars. We made a final trip to a fairly stinky port-a-loo then dragged our mattresses from the smaller tents round to the open. I have a complete phobia about snakes and after our experiences in Egypt I was less than keen on scorpions too. We set our beds up next to each other and I climbed into my pyjamas and sleeping bag hoping I got no uninvited creatures sleeping with me. Quietly, different members of our group started to drag their own mattresses into the Bedouin tent. Before long almost all our group had their beds set up in a line under the stars. I nodded off to the sound of Robert snoring and Bart snuffling.

Half way through the night I woke up desperate for a pee. I considered the option of walking fifty metres in the dark, alone to the stinky port-a-loo and decided it was never going to happen. I waited until I was desperate, then I wriggled out of my sleeping bag, hunted around for my shoes and fumbled along the tent to get away from everybody else. I had found my sandals but I wasn't going far from the tent.

Mission accomplished, I crept back towards the family and, with only the stars for lighting, fell straight over a bundle of cushions and old carpets, finally ending up back at my sleeping bag and gingerly putting my feet into it in case something else had crawled into the warmth. After that I slept well but woke at first light and went in search of some firewood around 5 am. There were several other early risers and we got the fire going, made mint tea and watched the sun rise.

There was no sign of any guards around and I wondered where they slept. I looked down, rather embarrassed at the wet in the sand that I knew had been made by me. The sun had not risen enough to dry it, but then I consoled myself that there were several other wet patches around that I wasn't responsible for! My 'mark' was next to the bundle of rags I had tripped over in the night. For some reason I had a hyperactive and impulsive moment of my own and I kicked the cushions, which to my alarm grunted back at me. One of the guides had slept with us in the tent and he was buried under this mound of old carpets and cushions. Thankfully he was so hung over with drunken sleep that he had missed my peeing episode next to his feet, slept through me falling over him and snored on as I kicked him in the morning. I wished I could sleep that well!

On our last day we took a boat trip along the coast from Akabar and then returned to have our final dinner with Samier our guide. Bart was delighted when the rest of the group volunteered him to present Samier with his gift and say thanks from us. I urged Bart to write a few words down so that he wouldn't 'freeze' when the time came, but in his usual "I know better" way he declined. Imagine my surprise when after dinner he delivered a very eloquent five minute speech that was thoughtful and funny and straight from the heart. The others applauded Bart and my eyes filled with tears of joy. Though only a little thing on the surface of it, we had been through dark times of doubt and criticism and here was the start of a man emerging from a boy.

We returned to the hotel and Bart and his Dad went to our room to start to pack whilst I stayed down in the bar for a drink with a few of the group. One person I had spent little time talking to on the trip was the military doctor. His wife was pleasant enough but he tended to keep himself to himself, which was fair enough. I sat with the two lovely nurses and Hazel, the eighty year old who had the body and mind of a sixty year old. They asked me about ADHD and the drugs that were available and at some point I was conscious of the doctor joining us. I had just finished relating the story about Bart's heart incident and also the fact that he had grown eight inches in the ten months since he had stopped taking the drug.

Hazel asked me if there were any more natural treatments that might help and we started to talk about the fatty acids, calcium and magnesium supplements that Bart took. The doctor started to join in the discussion and delivered a monologue on there being no evidence of the effect of these supplements for improving behaviour of ADHD children. The rest of us were pretty stunned at the forcefulness of his speech – it was unnecessary and uninvited. Sometimes I felt very vulnerable as a mother. You always try to give one hundred and fifty per cent to get it right and make the right decision for your children, but I am very aware that often it is only time that shows us if we made the best choices or not. I had always felt guilty about permitting doctors to prescribe medication for Bart, even though I knew he couldn't have survived the state school system without some medical intervention. I often felt 'judged' by individuals that came into contact with Bart and I felt that I fell short of their expectations.

The hurt expression must have told my friends that I was upset by his comments and both Hazel and the nurses started to quiz the doctor about his first hand experience of such things as he was a military doctor. He admitted that he had no personal knowledge, but he felt that as a doctor his opinion was more valued than my own experiences. He sat and criticised my theory about fatty acid supplements – even though it has been well documented and research suggested it could benefit individuals. What he was saying was 'I am the doctor and I know best – you are only the parent'. I excused myself from the conversation and made it to my room before starting to cry. I didn't cry because my pride was hurt, having a son like Bart left little room for pride, but I cried because of the prejudice. Not for the first time in my life people who knew nothing about the reality of living with an ADHD child felt bold enough to stand in judgement. It was Liz who wrapped her arms around me and told me what a good mum she thought I was and that she believed I could make a difference.

The following morning as I went down for breakfast I met the doctor's wife. She was embarrassed and apologised for her husband's behaviour, blaming some of it on his military background. I said she really didn't need to apologise because she had no reason to. I didn't add that I thought her husband was too spineless to see that he did! Having the confidence to believe you can make a difference for your children is a valuable and precious thing and its fragility as a state of mind means it can be damaged by opinionated know-alls who sometimes know very little.

Chapter 22

Strangles and Graffiti

That spring the riding stables where my daughter rode was quarantined due to an outbreak of strangles. The name sounds worse than it is, but it is unpleasant none the less and deemed serious enough in the horsy world to close a yard to horses entering or leaving until the all clear is given by the veterinary. There were over seventy horses and ponies in the yard and because they didn't all catch strangles together it meant that we had to wait for over four months before we got the all clear and people could take their horses out hacking and competing again. There had been a good atmosphere whilst we were in quarantine. Competitions and fun events had been arranged for people like me who were better at the egg and spoon race on horseback than they were at serious riding.

To celebrate our freedom the owner of the yard organised an evening in the local village hall with music, karaoke and bring your own drink. The evening was great fun and everybody was in a celebratory state. Liz and Bart came and Liz spent most of her time dancing and trying to sing whilst Bart whizzed around outside in a state of great excitement. The hall was next to St Thomas's, the first school Bart had attended and we stood outside the hall looking across at the place he and I had so many unhappy memories of. After a very funny evening where even I joined in the karaoke, we walked home across the fields in a merry state and left our car in the school car park. Bart had been a bit hyper but generally well behaved which meant I had been able to enjoy the evening.

It was a few days later when one of the girls who worked in the yard spotted me arriving and told me that Jo, the lady who ran the yard, was looking for me. She had a very straight face and somehow I knew I had done something wrong, but I couldn't figure out what. I knocked on the door and Jo answered, invited me in and proceeded to take out a rather lengthy letter from an envelope. The letter was from the local Parish Council and started off by informing her that the riding school was no longer welcome to hire the village hall in the future. It went on to list damage that had occurred during the evening.

I racked my brains as she read – I wasn't aware that we had broken anything or caused any damage and the evening had been pretty harmless. It was when she mentioned the word "school" that I began to understand where this was going. Apparently there had been some damage done to St Thomas's school next door. Two broken windows, one large and one small, upended pots that had been growing beans and graffiti on the side of the school building. Not conclusive, I thought, if Bart had anything to do with it – which I very much hoped he didn't – it would be hard to prove. Jo smiled, almost with relief and admitted that she thought it might be her daughter, who had attended St Thomas's at the same time as Bart, but it was what was written on the school building that rather suggested someone else. "Your school sucks, Bart Nickells rules OK" in very large writing had been left for all to read. I couldn't wait to get hold of Bart. I apologised profusely and then Jo's face broke into a big smile. She knew Bart well and had done her fair share of reprimanding him for leaping off the hay bales in the barn, but somehow I think she understood.

I went home and in search of Bart. I had the letter with me and I accosted him as soon as he came into my sight line. Bart didn't deny it, he let me rant off about poor behaviour and lack of maturity then he turned those big blue eyes on me and asked me what had given him away? I thought for a moment and then replied "Well son, signing your name was not your brightest move!"

I felt guilty about the damage because Bart had done the wrong thing, but underneath I really understood what he felt. He had endured a very miserable three and a half years at that school. He had left it with a stammer, no self confidence and other problems that a seven year old boy shouldn't experience. I could hardly blame him for his actions; we had given him the opportunity. I hadn't supervised him enough and he had the motive.

We sent a cheque to the school and a letter saying that we had been at the party but were not aware of anything untoward happening. Though Bart never saw, I did laugh about the situation and his honesty in saying what he thought and signing his name. Secretly, though I have never told Bart this. I wish I had seen what he had written and had the balls to sign my name right alongside his!

Chapter 23

More Trouble at School and Home

Bart really was shooting up in height. Aged nearly thirteen he had grown significantly taller than either his sister or me. It had long become inappropriate to threaten Bart with anything other than removal of rewards and treats. Bart was starting to gain some sense of "What if?" which meant that although he was still highly impulsive, he did at least recognise that actions had consequences. At school he had a relatively small band of friends, mainly boys that he hung around with and also got into trouble with.

Before school and during break times were the two occasions when neither I nor the school could predict what they would get up to. This was a recurring nightmare for me, never knowing what the next 'phone call would bring. One morning I was sitting at my desk around 8.30 am. I was always in early to work as I am a morning person and can get a lot done before the day's events take over my day. My mobile rang and I looked at the display screen – no caller i.d. This usually meant it was one of the teachers at De Leeds trying to catch up with me.

Our office had a wireless network which ensured our computers worked anywhere in the building, but it also had an adverse effect on mobile phones, which cut out, leaving vital bits of conversations unheard. I always had a feeling of foreboding when I knew it was Bart's school on the line and would scurry off to a quiet place to hear the news. My favourite hide out was the disabled toilet, where reception was excellent and it gave privacy if I found the urge to have a cry.

I retreated from the office answering the 'phone as I went. "Mrs Nickells?" the voice spoke on the other end "Its De Leeds School here. Your son is on his way to hospital in an ambulance!"

No amount of knowledge of Bart's nature, or pep talks to him every morning on the 'phone, ever prepared me for the calls I got about him. Every time the school rang me it was a different situation that I had to react to. This time Bart had been mucking about with his friends in the part of the school grounds that were strictly off-bounds. He had been climbing and had fallen out of a tree. He was having difficulty breathing and pains in his chest. The school suspected bruised or cracked ribs and his father was not available on the home line so they had called for an ambulance and he was on his way to hospital. Bart didn't carry a mobile phone; he had been bought several which always ended up lost, stolen or washed in the pockets of his trousers. I had no way to get hold of him to find out how he was and no choice but to leave the office, and my well ordered day of meetings, to go and track down Bart in the county hospital. As it happened Bart, when I eventually found him, was bruised but fine, but my day was shredded.

In most lessons the teachers at De Leeds had the upper hand with Bart. Providing he was placed near the front of the class it was fairly easy to keep an eye on him. He had long since grown out of getting up and wandering round the classroom when he was bored and he had now turned his attention to finely tuning his mimicking skills.

Bart had the most amazing geography teacher at De Leeds, Mr Jenks, who had been awarded the OBE for his outstanding efforts raising money for under privileged children in Africa. I particularly liked the teacher because of his kind, non judgemental and relaxed approach to Bart. When we met at parents evening his soft Welsh lilting voice would inform us that Bart had a particular strength in the subject of geography – he just needed to apply himself a bit more.

Every year this teacher organised a school trip to Africa where the students from De Leeds could go for three weeks to do building and other voluntary work for this excellent cause. Reflecting, this must have been really difficult for Mr Jenks. A lot of the De Leeds pupils were unruly and it must have been quite stressful keeping tabs on them so far from home. During one parents evening the subject of the Africa trip came up. I said that I thought it would do Bart good to go and help others, but somehow Mr Jenks' smile glazed over and he mumbled something about it being too much responsibility to look after Bart. I fully understood and respected his honesty and confided that I often felt a bit like that myself when we took Bart on holiday!

Mr Jenks was quite a religious man and did not tolerate bad language in the class. One day I got an e mail from him to say that Bart had really let himself down in class. Wondering what could have happened I quizzed Bart when we got home that evening. From the way Bart was smiling I knew this was going to be naughty but probably amusing.

Bart said that Mr Jenks had been telling the class about his next trip to Africa and looking for recruits. One boy had asked "How much does it cost sir?" to which Mr Jenks replied "Only £1,300". Quick as a flash and with his best Catherine Tate voice Bart had said "One thousand and three hundred pounds – what a fu*king liberty!" The class had exploded in fits of laughter and Mr Jenks had stood there horrified. I don't think he knew who Catherine Tate was, let alone watched an episode of her show.

Not for the first time in my life I was completely embarrassed for the teacher and yet could really see the funny side, at the same time. I made a phone call and sent three emails to Mr Jenks trying to explain the context of Bart's comment and the fact that he was, albeit inappropriately, mimicking a popular TV show and not being deliberately rude. I was never sure if Mr Jenks fully understood but I do believe he forgave Bart.

One other area where Bart could not be trusted was the metal work room. At home Bart had been allowed to use all sorts of machinery, with the supervision of his father and with no incidents. However in the school environment Bart lost what modicum of common sense he possessed. Whether he was playing the fool or just curious is not clear, but Bart had numerous 'incidents' in the school labs and work rooms and it led to several conversations between home and school. On one occasion Bart was wearing a 'fat face' t-shirt under his school shirt, both of which he chewed up in the belt sander. I am still quite amazed that he was ever allowed to continue wood work or metal work classes.

Going anywhere that is out of bounds is probably a common lure for most adolescent boys and mine was no exception. Access to the school playing fields was forbidden at break times as it was impossible to supervise the kids when they were too far from the school building – yet a group of them would consistently court detention and exclusion by taking every opportunity to escape. Bart did his fair share of detentions for this crime and once announced that the best time was when it was low cloud or misty. Apparently these conditions meant he could pull his school blazer over his head, run like hell and become invisible after only a few yards. It was just a harmless game to him, one of the many rules that were set in place to be tested.

At home 'being invisible' meant playing on the other side of the hill so he wasn't visible from the garden, especially when Bart had friends round. Despite the 'ground rules for playing at home' talk, things would always end up getting out of hand, with someone being hurt, torn clothes, damaged property or the odd fire.

On one occasion Bart had two friends over and the three of them set off up the hill to play. I allowed them to take an old saw and a small axe as their favourite pass time was building a camp. I wasn't daft enough to think they wouldn't get into trouble and I had popped up the hill a couple of times to check all was well. I was peacefully doing a bit of gardening when a very red faced guy, from the builders next door, appeared in my garden and informed me that rocks were raining down on the roof of their warehouse.

I never took sides or apologised to anyone until I had the facts, so I thanked him and went in search of Bart and his friends. I rounded them up and asked them what they had been doing. Bart informed me that they had run a 'commando' raid on one of the builder's portacabins and stolen a ball of string. No one owned up to throwing any rocks, but when I went up the hill and looked down on their warehouse I could see the evidence in front of me, rocks of all shapes and sizes were spread across their corrugated roof. I was disgusted with Bart and his friends' behaviour. Having fun was one thing but this could have caused real harm to someone.

Bart's friends seemed to take it as a bit of a joke and disappeared off into the house to get changed. I told Bart to inform them that they were to go over and apologise to the builder's yard or they went home straight away. One of the two boys told Bart that there was no way he was 'effin' apologising so I told him to get his stuff and I would drop him off home. He looked at me for a long while then pulled on his shirt and they went over to apologise. I would imagine this was a novel experience for them and I watched them actually enter the building to make sure they didn't duck out.

Later, when they had both gone home, I told Bart I wanted a letter of apology from each of them. After a few days I received one letter but not one from the other boy. I told Bart he would never be welcome in the house again and he has never been since. The boy's father 'phoned me in an attempt to smooth things over and he said that whilst he admired my attitude he had never been able to make his son do anything he didn't want to. I was shocked by his approach; the boys were only thirteen years old. I also felt I could have taken the easy option years ago and just let Bart run riot. It would have reduced my stress levels but would not have helped Bart in the long run. I didn't take on the task of parenting lightly and continued to believe that I could make a difference despite the ups and downs.

Chapter 24

The Tour de France.

Robert had been a keen cyclist in his younger days and he always followed the Tour de France on the television. That summer we took him on a surprise weekend to Paris to see the final stage. A nice chilled weekend was what we all needed. But what we needed and what we got were two different things and our usual 'being in the wrong place at the wrong time' seemed more prevalent than ever!

We had taken the train to Paris and checked into our hotel up on a hill overlooking the city. We were meeting Mandy, a girlfriend of mine, who was cycling from Paris to London to raise money for Great Ormond Street Hospital, and I thought it might be a good idea to have a walk around to explore and work up a bit of an appetite.

We set off down the hill and soon found ourselves in a street market with stands selling fabulous fresh fruit and veg. There was a commotion up ahead and smoke billowing out of a restaurant shop front. We were herded past by the police and heard a siren coming from behind us. The fire brigade was attempting to reach the scene but the market stalls were blocking their entrance. A few moments later an ambulance crew jogged past us carrying a fully covered body on a stretcher. We had only been in Paris a couple of hours and already we had been near a tragic accident.

Next we went to the Rue de Rivoli to meet Mandy. From here there was an organised boat trip on the River Seine and dinner on the first level of the Eiffel tower which Bart was massively excited about since he had seen the James Bond movie 'View to a Kill', featuring that restaurant.

We were dropped by coach at the Eiffel Tower and were just waiting in a queue to board the next lift when we heard shouting and whistles blowing and the next thing we were surrounded by armed police with large machine guns. In the frantic hustle we were separated from the rest of the group and found ourselves being herded towards the park – I for one was not going to argue with the police and told Bart to wind his neck in and try not to get separated. We waited as the armed troops stormed the tower and we saw hundreds of tourists being evacuated from all of the entrances. We sat in the park and shared the ear plugs of Liz's ipod, passing the time guessing what the other person was listening to.

At first we thought there was a terrorist threat, then after about an hour we saw a single figure high up on the outside of the Eiffel tower, climbing upwards. Below were the troops and it appeared that rather than being blown to pieces, we were about to witness someone jumping from the tower. Liz, Mandy and I kept our backs to the scene whilst Bart looked on in morbid curiosity.

After another hour had passed the climber was apprehended and rescued from his precarious perch. We were allowed to leave the park and we walked across to the river to see if we would find the rest of our party. By chance we spotted a lady in a tight leopard skin dress that had been on the coach with us. We walked up and found our group who had just finished the river boat trip! I tried to explain to the tour guide that we had got stuck behind a police barricade and he told me that we weren't in his party anyway!

Confusion sorted, we had missed our time slot at the Eiffel tower, missed the boat ride and were hustled straight to a mediocre restaurant up the Champs Elysees. Bart didn't seem to mind missing the tour of the Eiffel tower as he had found the display of police and military far more entertaining.

The following day was the final stage of the 2004 Tour de France and Lance Armstrong looked like he was going to win it for the seventh time. Bart got dressed into his US postal cycling outfit and we set off early to find a space to get a good view on the Champs Elysees. We bought a picnic on the way of pastries, salad and bread and we found a great spot with a good vantage point to see the riders. We had a five hour wait in the baking sunshine but I was sure it would be worth it.

Finally, about twenty minutes before the race made its first circuit up the Champs Elysees, two things happened. Bart disappeared and a man fell off the ledge of a building about twenty feet away from us and broke his arm. My husband is a trained first aider so he relinquished his place by the barriers and fought his way through the crowd to help the guy.

The ambulance people thought that because we were helping we were related and after a bit of confusion Bart appeared and went off on his father's shoulders looking for the man's wife. With hundreds of thousands of people there, the chances of finding her were zilch – except for the fact that she was American and was wearing a white Stetson hat.

Bart and Rob spotted the wife about 200 yards on the other side of the Champs Elysees and made their way through the crowds to her and reunited her with her husband. Robert returned to watch the cycling to find he had lost his place, no one was going to let him through the crowd and Bart went missing again!

The guy in front of me took issue to the fact that I was drinking a beer in the blistering heat, then we heard police whistles behind us and the whole crowd turned to see what the trouble was. Of course it was Bart, stuck about twenty feet up a plane tree with his legs swinging either side of a large bough in his Lance Armstrong cycling kit, complete with cap turned sideways.

I am not sure how he had got up the tree, but with a bit of shouting from about eight policemen he soon shinned down. The crowd roared applause at the 'naughty boy', I went red, Bart couldn't get to the front so he missed most of it and I was so tired I just wanted to sit on the pavement. Another trip that didn't go according to plan!

Chapter 25

The Wedding

That autumn one of our old nannies was married and we were invited to the wedding. It was Lovely Lorry Lorraine, who had been so kind and patient with Bart in his earlier years. We stayed down in Wells, as the wedding was at the Bishop's Palace because Lorraine was marrying the Bishop's son 'Scrapheap', so nicknamed because he built working models and had appeared on several 'Scrapheap' TV programmes.

The wedding was medieval fancy dress and the bride and groom looked fabulous dressed as a knight and a maiden. Robert went as a jester, decked in a fabulous yellow and red outfit, whilst I went as Blackadder.....

We had a great time, but the following morning things took a turn for the worse. Bart was very down, grumpy and obnoxious. It's difficult to know how much of this behaviour was ADHD and how much was just growing up, but his mood swings at that time were pretty violent and he could be happy one minute and almost morose the next. We were having breakfast when Bart started to get really awkward. I was tired and I lost my patience and ordered him out of the dining room into a hallway.

Normally we would have had a short exchange through clenched teeth then everything would fall back into balance, but today was different, Bart was really angry. I have always maintained that it was useless to get into an argument with Bart as, although this sounds stupid, you would never win and the situation would spiral out of control. On this occasion I didn't heed my own advice and we had a row. Bart was so rude I reached out and slapped him before I had thought what I was doing. I turned to walk away and in retaliation Bart thumped me, hard, twice on the back. It physically knocked the wind out of me, but it also crossed into a place we had never been in our relationship.

I found a cloakroom and hid myself away and sobbed. I was hurt and angry and I had had enough. I felt that after all the love and extra miles I had walked for Bart, all the battles where I had been his champion, now we were reduced to this. I feared for the future of the family, we already trod a fine line of balance. It was easier for me, as the mum to follow the 'no blame policy', but for Liz and Robert it was hard and sometimes I asked them to forgive the unforgivable.

Eventually I found my way back to the breakfast table, still red faced from crying and it was clear from Bart's demeanour that his father had spoken some strong words to him. We walked round Wells and watched the annual bath race in the moat. We met people from the wedding and the bride and groom were in one of the races. Outwardly I maintained a cheery smile, but inwardly I was crying and still reeling from that morning's exchange.

I tried to rationalise it in my head and came to the conclusion that I was very much in the wrong – I should never have lashed out, but, likewise, neither should Bart and I was not sure I could forgive him. Bart was very quiet for the rest of the day. I tried to avoid him, both eye contact and physical contact, but sometime that afternoon I felt his hand slip into mine and a quiet "I'm sorry mum". I was never able to stay angry with Bart for long and although he did some infuriating and hurtful things he was always genuinely sorry after the event.

However, the mood swings stayed with us over the next couple of days and he lost his temper badly one evening when his dad was out and Liz and I were alone in the house. This time I was so concerned I locked the pair of us in the bathroom until I could hear that Bart had gone out for a walk to let off steam. Allowing him out when he was in such a rage meant he was a possible danger to himself and others. He might just walk blindly into the road and cause an accident. I had to weigh this up with the more immediate harm that could affect the family and on this occasion I let him go.

The police brought him back around 10 pm. They had found him wandering along the side of the main road about a mile from home. We thanked them, played the situation down and after a few words of advice for Bart they left. Bart was pretty tearful and still very anxious but his anger had left him and I just sat and hugged him. As is often the case – When they least behave like it – they need you most.

Quite by chance we had a meeting at CAMHS the following day, with yet another lay doctor, to see how Bart was progressing on his new medication. I was up in town working, but I was worried for his and our welfare so I gave a quick call to CAMHS and left a message with the receptionist that I was concerned about Bart's temper and violent mood swings.

At 5 pm we rolled up for our usual fifteen minute appointment. There was a new doctor that we hadn't met before and we all sat down to discuss Bart's progress. The doctor asked a few preliminary questions then focussed on Bart and I was gobsmacked by what I heard. Within ten minutes Bart had admitted to hearing voices and hallucinating. We were ushered from the room and for thirty minutes Bart and the doctor talked alone. I was not privy to what was said but after waiting outside we were called back in and the doctor asked us to take a seat.

He didn't beat around the bush. He told us that, in his opinion, Bart was severely depressed and frightened; he was hearing voices and seeing things. He said that he thought this was linked to Bart's medication and that there had been four suicide attempts by youngsters taking the drug. Depression was a side effect and he wanted Bart to stop taking the drug and he prescribed a six month course of Prozac, the antidepressants!

I couldn't believe what I was hearing, his mood swings were suddenly explained. He was frightened that he was losing his marbles and we were the ones handing out the drugs that were causing his anxiety.

I listened to all the reasons as to why Bart must take the antidepressants. Three times I said that I was not happy to switch from one drug to the next and three times I was told that Bart was depressed and it was essential that he be given them. I left with the prescription in hand, but not before I had told the doctor that I intended to stop Bart's ADHD medication immediately and that I did not plan to 'cash' the prescription unless absolutely necessary.

Bart had been on medication from seven to fourteen, half his life, and I was not about to allow him to become dependent on any more drugs – it was time for the real Bart to stand up. Blow the educational system and some teachers who encouraged yet more tablets, the veiled threats in the past that Bart would be out of full time mainstream education unless he continued to take his medication, the judgemental views from so called 'experts' who treated us as if we had subnormal IQs. This was my son and I would stand by him through anything, but drugs and their side effects were no longer an option.

I wrote to every single teacher in Bart's school. I wrote to the head master and his head of special needs. I explained exactly why Bart would no longer be taking his medication. I asked them for their support. The letter was sad and had I been in their position I would have been full of empathy for this family. It was interesting to see who did and did not respond to it, not because I was particularly bothered, just interested in my perception of people.

Walter, Bart's head of special needs, was one of those who did respond. He was amazingly supportive during and after Bart's secondary education and I will always be grateful for his willingness to walk the extra mile for Bart.

Chapter 26

Thrills, Trust and Growing Up

For our next family holiday adventure I decided on Peru. I am not sure what drew me to this option, but years before I had seen a picture of the lost site of Machu Picchu and I had dropped heavy hints to Robert that I would like to go there, only to find out that I was pregnant with Liz and would not be going anywhere in the near future. But good things come to those who wait, so after the usual trauma with Liz in the doctors waiting for our jabs, we set off on our latest adventure.

As usual I was exhausted from work and the last minute packing left us short on some essentials, but with the excitement of visiting a new continent we flew off to America where we would pick up our connecting flight to Peru.

The turn round time at Atlanta was only just over one hour and we knew it was a bit tight, but the travel agent had assured us that there was plenty of time. It didn't help much when, by the time we had taxied to our gate we only had fifty-five minutes to spare. There was no priority given for connecting flights and we finally got into the immigration hall to find that we were almost the last in line.

Picking the right queue reminds me of shopping in the supermarket. It's a lottery, you think you have picked the quickest checkout and it turns out to be the slowest and as usual I picked the wrong queue. U.S.A. immigrations were implementing a new system of eye scanning and it seemed to take forever for the people to be processed in front of us. When we were nearly at the front I realised that we only had fifteen minutes to make the connecting flight. I asked a group in front of us if they would mind if we pushed in and they didn't so the family all had their right eye photographed and we were through.

Next followed finding the right place to transfer and off came the shoes for the X-ray. There were ten minutes left as we sprinted along travellators, shoes in hand and finally made it to the gate. Surprisingly we were not the last on board, but I think we were well out of American air space before I got my breath back.

It was a five hour flight to Lima and we landed around one in the morning with that awful feeling of disorientation you get with long haul. The following day we set off in our little coach, a small party of fourteen, to discover Peru.

The scenery changed as the bus climbed up the side of the Andes and we were warned about the dangers of altitude sickness and shown the oxygen bottle at the back of the bus that we all hoped we would never have to use.

One of the first stops was on the way to Cocla Canyon. We were dropped for an 'easy walk' just after lunch with a plan to be back at the hotel in a couple of hours. Unfortunately the guide got lost and so did we. After four hours of clambering over some 'not so easy' terrain we still didn't know where we were going. The light was starting to go and the temperature was dropping from a balmy 20 degrees to freezing. Finally we saw the lights of the village; we were on the final weary stage of the walk.

There was a deep gorge between us and the village and the only way across was a narrow foot bridge used by the villagers. Unfortunately it was also used by the farmers to bring their livestock in for the night and just as we stepped onto the bridge someone behind shouted "watch out" and a bull came careering round the bend, closely followed by a couple of its friends. Jumping for high ground we watched as the cattle stampeded across the bridge followed by a few goats and their owners. We were all suffering from the cold as we had dressed for a sunny expedition and the temperature was dropping fast.

Once back in our rooms I made the mistake of not diving into the shower immediately and, by the time I did get in, the water came out as a cold trickle. That evening I sat at the dinner table in three fleeces with my back to a log fire and my teeth chattering. Bart, Liz and Robert seemed to have warmed up a bit quicker, but on returning to our rooms it was clear that the heating was not up to much and, as I was sharing with Liz, we pushed the twin beds together and doubled our bedding in an attempt to keep warm. The following morning was crisp and bright. The socks and knickers I had washed the night before and hung out to dry were frozen and Bart came screeching into the room and took me to inspect a giant icicle that was hanging down from the solar heating panels!

After breakfast we took the coach up to a viewing point in the Colca canyon where the condors fly. We had only just settled into a spot when above the canyon, large raven like birds started to glide towards us on the thermals. I watched through my binoculars as the birds approached and adjusted the focus. It was only when the condors flew over us that I realised I couldn't get the whole bird into view and I dropped my binoculars. The full size of these birds was enormous and they had an almost prehistoric presence. They flew no more than fifty feet above our heads and even I, who rarely managed to get the subject in the viewfinder of my camera, managed to get some terrific shots. The fact that they have a four metre wing span may have helped me a little as well!

We walked for a while along the edge of the canyon and I made sure I had Bart in my sight as the guide told stories about locals going over the edge never to be seen again! The floor of the canyon was one thousand feet below and I had no intention of letting go of Bart around here.

We continued our journey towards Lake Titicaca and the high altitude and long hours spent on the road gave us a sense of light headedness. I pointed out glaciers and glacial features until Bart spoke very loudly in the bus, something to the effect that if he saw another U shaped valley he would go f***ing mad. After that the bus went a bit quiet and I retreated into one earpiece of

Liz's ipod. As we drove on towards Lake Titicaca we sang along to "I'm going slightly mad" by Queen, which has remained a favourite song of mine!

I don't think any of us had any preconceptions of what Lake Titicaca was like, but it was the most amazing and surreal experience. We took a boat out to the Uros islands, which are basically made up of one metre deep reed beds. The islands are actually floating and if you fall out with your neighbour you can just cut your island in half and drift away. What a civilized way of living, I thought!

We spent the morning on one of these islands with a couple of families. There was no electricity, no running water – apart from the lake, and it was one of the most peaceful places on earth. They gave us a demonstration about living on the islands, fishing, lighting fires and the commute by boat to the school island. Again I watched Liz and Bart take this serene way of life on board and contrast it to their own way of life. I half fancied I could live there, away from the bustle of modern life, but the thought of Bart starting a fire soon dampened my day dream.

From there, we took the train on a ten hour journey down to Cusco. It was a steam train which caused great excitement for the boys and it had a viewing carriage at the back with a bar, which was highly exciting for me! The train trundled across the high altiplano at what seemed like little more than walking pace. Soon after setting off we approached a town. The train sounded its whistle and the market stalls that were set out on the track were moved aside as the train passed. Displays of fruit were left between the tracks, then seamlessly the market came back together again as the train passed. It was rather like watching a human zipper in action.

It was a good place to get to know some of our group and over coffee, lunch and a glass of wine we got chatting. I became friends with a lady called Lesley who was travelling alone and as we stood at the back of the train watching the ever changing scenery, we discovered that she lived only twenty miles from our home and was a head mistress of a junior school. We got talking about my children and I told her about Bart's ADHD and the fun we had experienced with the education system. She may have been being kind, but she said she had pupils in her school with ADHD and she had no idea that Bart had it too. I felt grateful and realised that Bart was moving on and growing up. When you live with something every day it is hard to see change, but fresh eyes often see things we don't. Our family adopted Lesley on that holiday and we have been great friends since.

Towards the end of our holiday we spent a few days in Machu Picchu which was another experience that I won't forget. We arrived the first day and all took the bus which rattled up a steep road with many hairpin bends. Our guides took us round for a guided tour and then we returned to our hotel, tired and nibbled by small black flies that were everywhere.

The railway line comes right down the central road in the town of Aguas Calientes. People hustle and bustle along using the track as a thoroughfare until a train approaches. Robert and Bart are particularly fond of steam trains and as all the restaurants were mainly located along that stretch we decided to eat out on the pavement or platform, whichever.

Lesley joined us and her only request was that we picked somewhere quiet. Most of the tourists were still up at the lost city so we more or less had the place to ourselves until a train chuffed its way noisily down the track and parked right next to us. Steam hissed, smoke belched out of the huge funnel and the noise was almost deafening. It was Peru's equivalent of the Orient Express and we watched as the well-heeled and rich disembarked. Our 'quiet' cafe table had turned into the middle of a noisy station.

The following morning we were up and waiting for the first bus at six. We climbed up to Machu Picchu and then met our guide who explained that we could either take a gradual climb up to the sun gate to see the fantastic views back down the valley, or we could climb up Wayna Picchu which was a smaller 'sugar loaf' pointed mountain that, from the angle I was looking at, looked very scary and dangerous. Bart said he wanted to climb Wayna Picchu and I said absolutely not, so he disappeared in a strop. I felt it was too dangerous to risk and although he could climb like a goat, he still had a very impulsive temperament.

There was also another lad on the trip, of similar age and I knew that there would be a competitive edge between them to see who could get to the top first. The Wayna Picchu group got ready to set off, Bart continued to sulk and Robert reasoned with me. He has a fear of heights and can't look down from the top of a five storey building without suffering from vertigo, but here he was arguing that he and Bart should do the climb! I thought he was mad and talked through the risks but I realised that I couldn't protect Bart from everything forever. He needed to take responsibility for himself, to learn about risk taking and the implications – even if they could be life threatening.

Reluctantly I changed my mind and my heart was in my throat as I watched him and his Dad rush along to catch up with the rest of the group. Liz and I picked up the rucksacks and set off on the gentler climb to the sun gate. It took us about an hour to get up to the top and when we looked down on Machu Picchu and Wayna Picchu the view was indeed stunning. The walk had relaxed me, but I felt a small knot of fear for Bart's safety in the pit of my stomach.

We sat a while and tried to identify the colourful birds that bobbed about on the tree canopy and then we made the descent and went in search of the boys. For about half an hour I couldn't find anybody who was with our party, but just as I was making my way towards the exit and cafe I saw Robert and Bart coming towards us. Bart was grinning from ear to ear – they had completed the climb in a good time. I was slightly alarmed, but not surprised, that Bart had beaten the group to the top and had passed others who had set off earlier. Clearly Rob had not managed to keep up with him.

Lesley joined us and thanked Bart for helping her near the summit. Apparently there had been a flat rock to cross with nothing to hold onto. She had felt this was a bit too challenging and had decided that she might go back down, but Bart had climbed above her and offered his hand to heave her up safely. She later admitted that she had "conquered one of her fears" as she was afraid of heights and Bart's support had made her carry on. I felt the usual mix of emotions, proud that Bart had helped Lesley, grateful that he had made it in one piece, concerned when he owned up to racing the other boy in the group and relieved that it was all over!

On the penultimate day of our holiday we went white water rafting which was a new experience for us, but we could all swim well and loved the water. We were kitted up with wet suits and helmets and then the guides started to instruct us on what we needed to do to stay in the boat. The instructor was about five minutes into his lesson when Liz whispered "I don't feel very well" and crumpled to the floor in a faint. Both Liz and Bart were very resilient as children. I had brought them up not to fuss unless they felt really ill, but seeing Liz as pale as porcelain I knew that something was wrong. It was a sunny day and we were hot standing around in our wet suits, so we sat her in the shade, with some water and the instructor carried on.

Within the group we sometimes found one aggravating individual. On this trip, we had a lady from Cardiff, in her forties, who had come on holiday with her boyfriend. She was one of those people who offended others just by opening her mouth. She had quite a judgemental manner and a bit of a chip on her shoulder and we had all been on the receiving end of one of her caustic comments during the holiday. Her partner, by contrast was mild mannered with a good sense of humour – a nice guy. She, though nearest, didn't move to help when Liz fainted, but turned to her partner and whispered "women's problems" in a loud stage whisper that the whole group could hear. Liz was embarrassed and so were the rest of the group, except me, I was angry. I fixed her with one of my iciest stares as I tended to Liz. The instructors asked us if Liz wanted to carry on or would she prefer to make the trip in the bus, but Liz was determined to go in the raft and I thought the breeze and cool water would do her good.

We set off in two boats and the rafting experience itself gave us a real adrenaline buzz, with forty minutes of hard work and excitement. Just keeping ourselves in the boat required a lot of physical effort as it rushed through the rapids. Bart and Liz were in their element and to be honest so was I! We were split into two groups with two instructors in each boat. Lesley had opted to come with us and we were intent on racing the other group. There was no room for passengers and as we saw the rapids coming towards us we all paddled like hell until the instructors told us not to. One of the rapid sequences was a grade three which means nothing to me, but was exciting all the same.

As the river widened we came towards the spot at which we would stop. The other dingy came alongside us and one of their crew flicked Bart out of the boat and into the icy waters. He clambered back in and war was started between the two boats which resulted in a lot of splashing with our oars and several men overboard – including the offending instructor!

After a barbecue lunch the coach set off for Cusco and Lesley and I sat chatting about stuff. I glanced across at

Liz who looked very pale, plugged into her ipod listening to music. After a few more minutes I glanced across at her again and realised she was just staring straight ahead, almost as if she was in a trance. I sat beside her and spoke to her, but she didn't respond so I started to shake her lightly by the shoulders. She stiffened with her eyes wide open, convulsed then collapsed. I shouted for the bus to stop as I was being thrown all over the place on the bumpy road.

We got Liz upright and our guide found the Peruvian equivalent of smelling salts. Liz continued to slump, still in a faint and I was starting to get really worried about her. She said she felt sick so I dragged her to a small loo cubicle at the back of the bus. The driver set off driving like a possessed man and I sat on the loo seat with Liz balanced on my knee. I braced myself and Liz and I lurched from side to side, in view of all on the bus as the loo door swung open and shut with the erratic driving. Not one of our more dignified moments.

We drove for half an hour at a crazy speed, overtaking everyone else on the road, till we reached a medical clinic on the outskirts of Cusco. It was shut so we carried on to the hotel where a doctor had been called. Still wedged in the loo, Liz and I bounced off the walls until we arrived at our hotel. One of our rafting instructors, who was over six feet tall and barefoot, picked Liz up and carried her, like a doll, from the bus to the hotel. The doctor arrived on his scooter a short time later and after examining her he left us with some pills and told Liz to rest. Our group all popped in to visit then went out to dinner for the last night, whilst I sat with Liz in the room with a packet of crisps and a lager. Not the greatest of ways to celebrate our last day of our holiday for Liz or me. The journey on the toilet was memorable but I was worried about Liz. Whatever she was suffering from was never diagnosed and went on for over a year – but that's another story!

Chapter 27

Work and Life Experience

Life back at home soon got into the routine of school and work. Bart was coming up to fifteen now and was doing his GCSE course work. Up until now I had always been able to help him with his studies and revision for SATS tests, but Bart was taking ten GCSEs and I was working full time so he had to fend for himself to some extent. Bart's organisational skills have left quite a bit to be desired over the years. ADHD means 'attention deficit' i.e. lack of concentration. If I had a pound for every time a teacher has said or written "Bart must remember...." I would not have needed to work as long as I have. The problem throughout Bart's education has been that teachers say ADHD, but many don't connect 'attention deficit' with poor concentration and forgetfulness.

Things were always going missing at school and home. Books, pencil cases, homework, keys and mobile 'phones were all lost with annoying frequency and I think that we have kept the local stationery shop in business over the years with the number of replacements we have bought. Missing school exercise books was Bart's speciality and he never completed a term, let alone a year, of any subject with the same exercise book he started with! This meant that when Bart was approaching exams he didn't have much (if any) written coursework to refer to for revision. To counteract this I bought the published work books for the subjects that Bart was studying, to act as reference and revision books.

Like Liz before, Bart was required to do a week's work experience as part of the curriculum. Despite Bart's reputation where I worked – tales of his escapades had lightened many a dull moment – I managed to persuade my boss to allow Bart to do a week's work experience with me. Luckily for me, part way through the week Bart was selected to attend a three day forensic course at the local university, so he only spent two days with me and managed not to disgrace himself or wreck the building.

For his second week, Bart worked at Virgin head office at Gatwick Airport. He had joined the air cadets about six months before and had met a guy there who was doing his private pilot's license. This guy worked for Virgin and hoped to train to be a pilot in the future. Bart really enjoyed that experience. I took him to Marks and Spencer to kit him out with a suit and the transformation was remarkable. The little boy who was always in the thick of trouble had transformed into a smart young man. Of course the process had been happening over the years, but with the constant demands of work and life, sometimes you don't register or notice change. He loved his work experience with Virgin and it fuelled his interest in aircraft.

Bart continued to attend the air cadets. At that point he was talking about joining the Marines when he was old enough. He seemed to respond well to the formal discipline and he became totally responsible for his uniform, which he would press to within an inch of its life. The other main attraction of the air cadets was getting the opportunity to get up in the air in a 'plane or glider. On one trip, the company went to Boscombe Down and all the cadets went for individual flights with an instructor. Bart returned absolutely full of it and he recounted his flight, blow by blow, to me that evening. The pilot asked him if he wanted to have a steady lesson with some instruction, a trip over Stonehenge to sight see, or some aerobatics. "Guess which one I chose mum?" he asked, I didn't have to think for many seconds, "The aerobatics" I replied. "Yup" he said, "and I got to take the controls as well!" That year Bart's birthday present was a couple of lessons!

Bart was only six months away from his GCSEs. He had all but dropped a double in manufacturing technology after a few issues with his teacher. Bart had always had an inbuilt people receptor which told him if people liked him or not. Some teachers believe they command respect simply because they are adults and teachers. But the best teachers are the ones who realised that respect is a two way street. You have to give something to get something.

This particular teacher was teaching a new GCSE subject. She rarely prepared much for the lesson and had few people skills, so the result was that the kids mucked around in class and little was learned. Bart didn't respect her and I don't think she liked him much. I was fascinated to meet her at one parents evening when she barely said hello to us before laying into Bart and telling him how naughty he was. She gushed like a tap, exposing examples of his poor behaviour and then sat back as if she had passed the buck to me and it was my turn now to berate him.

Bart sat there forlorn and in trouble, whilst she managed a sly smile of satisfaction. I am not sure whether she or Bart were more surprised when I quietly asked her what she was doing to help the situation? She asked me what I meant and I explained my two way street theory. I pointed out her body language, which was aggressive, and after ten minutes we agreed to wipe the slate clean. Bart would try really hard for her – if she would try really hard for him.

I had one more meeting with that teacher a few months later. Bart's relationship was on a downward spiral with her again. She was excluding him from lessons and the bottom line was that Bart was not learning. I asked for an appointment and I also asked Walter, Bart's head of special needs, to be present. I drew up an agenda of things I wanted to cover and I jotted down a précis of what Bart had been through over the past ten years of schooling.

The teacher arrived at the meeting, which was held in the schools broom cupboard, with a defensive and slightly aggressive attitude. Walter sat quietly as I went over what I wanted to cover. The whole class had failed its first year exam and would have to re-sit it again the following year with all of their other finals. Having gone through the agenda, I told her that I would like to read a couple of pages about Bart that I had prepared earlier.

She sat quietly as I read about Bart's early years at school, the fights we had experienced and the real achievements we had made. As I got towards the end of my summary, my voice wobbled and I knew I was very close to tears. I had shared our private experiences with her and I felt raw as I thought back to the demanding and difficult times we had been through. The teacher was also moved by our experiences and our relationship moved to a new and better level. I had taken a risk opening up to her, but the experience was valuable for both of us. I know some teachers must feel that the burden of discipline falls mainly upon the school and themselves, but it is important for them to recognise when a parent is truly walking the extra mile for their child and help them to get even further.

Chapter 28

Think Before You Act…

A few weeks after Bart's work experience I received another dreaded 'phone call from the school. There had been an incident with a group of boys and Bart had thrown a French banger firework at another boy, hitting him in the neck. Luckily the boy was not badly harmed but very shaken. The headmaster was debating exclusion or expulsion for the boys involved and meanwhile could I just come into school and collect Bart.

I cancelled all my meetings for the rest of the day and rushed for the next train from Victoria. I would need to go home first to collect my car and wouldn't be able to pick up Bart for another hour or so. All the way home I felt sick at the thought of what he had done and wondered if the police would be involved as the school had mentioned.

I arrived at De Leeds and went in search of Bart, who was sitting in a classroom alone. His first words were "I'm sorry Mum, I don't even know why I did it". I felt very let down by him and couldn't look him in the eye when I greeted him. I was very close to tears and I just wanted to be away from the school whilst my dignity was still nearly intact. To avoid meeting anyone we took the back route out of the school and as we rounded the corner of the main school building we walked straight into the headmaster. He and I had had our fair share of exchanges over the years and he was the last person I wanted to meet when I felt so vulnerable.

On this occasion, however, he surprised me. He spoke about the incident and I choked up. I just responded by nodding my head, unable to speak. He told me that there were several boys involved and he was regarding them with equal responsibility – he wasn't placing all the blame on Bart's shoulders, which had usually been the case for most of Bart's school career. Furthermore, the school did not intend to involve the police, although the parents of the injured boy might.

We didn't go straight home, we went for a drive and parked at a view point, at Bart's request. I sat in silence, as I had done so many times; waiting for Bart to tell me what was going on in his head. Eventually he started to speak and told me how the situation arose.

Apparently Bart was with a gang of boys in the playground and as usual desperate to seek their acceptance and approval. They outlined the plan of throwing a French banger and when Bart asked who was going to do the throwing they said "You"! And he did just that, without stopping to think about any of the consequences. This lack of forethought epitomised Bart's behaviour, but somewhere in the back of my mind I couldn't help thinking that some of Bart's friends had optimised on this behavioural trait. I think the head also suspected this and that was the reason he had excluded all of the boys involved, rather than singling out just Bart. He spoke about his actions and kept saying over and over again "I just don't know why I did it, I like him".

That evening Bart said he wanted to 'phone the boy, which I thought took great courage as it might not be well received. He made the 'phone call by himself and I warned him that he was likely to encounter two very angry parents. In fact the parents were far more reasonable than we could have hoped and Bart was able to talk to his friend and apologise.

Bart didn't 'phone him because he was hoping that the police wouldn't be involved, he 'phoned because he genuinely cared – although this seems like a contradiction against his earlier action. Thankfully the family decided not to involve the police. The injury was not too bad and the boy recovered quickly. Bart learnt an important message about the dangers of not thinking before you act and I got stuck with Bart at work for a week as there was no way I was going to leave him home alone during his exclusion from school.

I felt embarrassed and ashamed taking Bart to work. Work experience was one thing, but throwing a French banger at another boy was quite another. I decided to go and see James, my trading executive and just explain the situation, promise that Bart would be as quiet as the grave and that he wouldn't deter me from my job in any way. Bart asked me not to mention what he had done to be excluded from school, but I reasoned that if he was stupid enough to have done what he did, then I wasn't going to tell a lie for him.

My executive listened to what I had to say and then he called Bart into his office. I thought he was going to give Bart a dressing down for his behaviour, but he took a different approach and told Bart about a time when he had been excluded from school himself for punching a boy. Relieved, Bart smiled conspiratorially and I remember thinking that Bart didn't need to think that this made things OK. But what James was trying to say was, we all muck things up sometimes, but if we learn from our mistakes we can move on and become a bigger person. Bart learned from that experience and so did I.

Chapter 29

The Exams and School Ends

When we got Bart's timetable of exams I booked some time off to help prepare him for each exam. At first sight the exams looked as if they were all too close together and I was not sure that Bart would be able to cope with holding so many facts in his brain at the same time, but we had been revising the coursework since just after the Christmas break. I made special time to sit down and go through the work with Bart, but he had to sit the exams alone and it would be his work that resulted in passing or not.

The revision sessions really tested our relationship. From my perspective I was trying to fit a quart into a pint pot. Nobody covered my job for me when I was not there, so I had to plan ahead and make sure that things at work could carry on without me. Bart was outwardly bored by the repetition of revising and would often sit down to revise with me in a really bolshie mood. Sometimes I called Bart "Kevin", named after the Harry Enfield adolescent character who was as nice as pie one moment and going off on one in the next.

Bart usually sat down with good intentions, but as

he got older, he would often procrastinate about something quite trivial that I mentioned. This would develop into an argument and any thought of work or study went clean out of the window. In order to combat this tactic of Bart's, I had to remain very calm, even when he was sorely trying my patience with his comments or mannerisms. No one is perfect and though I strived to help him achieve, there were dark moments when I would have to walk away from him, for my sanity and his well being! On such occasions I would disappear into the garden with a large glass of wine and a cigarette and 'phone a friend or just sit and look at the plants until my patience and heart rate were restored and I could go back to Bart in a positive frame of mind.

One topic that tested both of us was science. Bart had done fairly well in his module exams, gaining mostly B's. He had opted to take the higher level GCSE in double science, but a few weeks before the exam he got cold feet and he talked about changing to an easier level. Whilst I have always strived to help Bart achieve, I am not a pushy parent who always wants their child to be the best in everything. To be honest, I was just relieved Bart was still in mainstream education and hadn't been sent to a special school for children with behavioural problems, so being first in everything was not on the Richter scale. However, Bart and I had been learning the syllabus to the higher level. Some of it seemed to be sticking in Bart's mind and I found I could quote all sorts of random facts on liver function, plant cells and the periodic table, that only enforced other people's view that I was raving bonkers!

I asked to see Bart's science teacher about the exam

and she felt that he would be safer to do the foundation exam as this would guarantee him two pass grades at least. I felt that if he didn't aim high he would never know what he might have achieved. In the end Bart took the higher papers. Though we had literally learnt the whole syllabus, we focussed on four topics from the previous year in the final revision session before his first exam. I picked Bart up afterwards and could tell it hadn't gone well but I asked anyway. "It was crap Mum" he replied. We had wasted the last revision session focussing on the wrong topics and he hadn't remembered all the other stuff we had covered.

We had a week to make amendments before the second exam and, as I felt responsible for the fact that he was taking the more difficult exams and I had made him focus on the wrong topics, I was determined that the second paper would go better for him. We read and re-read those damn topics until we were sick of them, but it paid off. Bart bounced home from his final science exam in a much more positive mood. He reckoned everything he knew came up, which was hardly surprising as he knew everything! All we had to do was wait until August for his results.

The last day of term and life at De Leeds had finally arrived. Bart came home from school with his white shirt covered with messages, (written all over it in felt tip pen), some of which were obscene! This was the end of one chapter in Bart's education and the start of another, but in-between, over the summer holidays, I had planned a holiday that would take us to the Galapagos Islands and the Amazon jungle. I reckoned that Liz was reaching the age where she would no longer want to come on family holidays and I decided to make our last one something to remember and we were certainly not disappointed! I had booked the entire holiday on the internet which on the face of it saved me a lot of money, but I am not renowned for my computer skills and I did wonder, as we set off, if I truly had everything in place.

We were flying out on the Thursday and Heathrow had ground to a halt on the previous week when police had arrested suspected terrorists. Flights were cancelled and seriously disrupted that week and I was worried that we might not get to Amsterdam in time to catch our flight out to Ecuador. I transferred the family to an earlier flight from Heathrow and we made our connection with plenty of time to shop, read and have a few drinks at Schipol Airport. The flight to Quito in Ecuador was around thirteen hours with a short stop to refuel, so I took a sleeping pill, had my meal with a couple of drinks and fell fast asleep. Bart woke me when we had touched down to refuel. The combination of working all that day, the drinks and sleeping pill, rendered me almost comatose, so the family disembarked and I remained curled up in my seat, fast asleep.

I vaguely remember waking for takeoff, but I dozed on until I became aware that the captain had been speaking in Dutch for quite some time. Out of the window I could see the most amazing electrical storm that seemed to illuminate the whole sky. Liz clutched my arm, she was on her own state of personal alert after the Heathrow activity the previous week and the lightening was not filling her with confidence – and then it got worse!

The pilot started his announcement in English and informed us that a volcano had erupted in Ecuador and that we were required to fly fifty miles around it to avoid potential risk. We were due to land at another airport in Ecuador before flying on to Quito, but this would not now happen due to volcanic ash in the vicinity. We were now flying direct to Quito, but would be unable to land until sunrise due to surrounding mountains. Fabulous!

After that I was wide awake, Liz was nearly hysterical and, for once in his life, Bart was quiet. As first light came up we started our descent. The plane seemed to carry on dropping, yet when we looked out of the windows there were mountain peaks on either side. The descent was steep over farms and houses that gradually gave way to Quito city. I am sure we flew down the high street before we touched down on the runway. I had booked us into a small bistro hotel and the first day we just lazed around and dozed, recovering from our night flight.

The following morning we packed up and headed back to the airport at 5.30 am to take a flight to the Galapagos Islands. The volcanic eruption had severely disrupted the airlines and initially the departure board said the flight was on time, but as we waited and the departure time came and went it was clear that this was not the case. Our biggest problem was that there were no announcements in English and we couldn't understand the departure boards, the airport was in chaos and those who did know where they were going seemed to barge past, regardless of personal space. People were missing flights, shouting and looking on bemused, clearly we were not the only people with problems.

I was reluctant to go to the loo in case I missed an announcement, but the queue was halfway round the departure lounge and I decided to get on the back of it. Liz and I waited patiently over the next hour as we gradually got closer to the loo door. When there were only about a dozen people in front of us a small round nun who had not been bestowed with the prettiest face, pushed roughly to the front of the queue announcing she was about to miss her plane. Most people let her through and those who didn't got barged to one side. I remember thinking that for a nun, she lacked grace and would do well in the national rugby team. She emerged without a thank you or a smile and the rest of us waited our turn.

One and a half hours later we met the same nun again on the plane we had just boarded. She and her fellow nuns had been given preferential boarding and they were already seated. As we passed her I glared at her and she just glared right back with no hint of remorse.

The flight was a couple of hours and on disembarking we followed the sign that said 'Foreigners this way' which made us all giggle! After a bit of a queue for passports, we transferred to a coach that dropped us at a shelter by the water's edge, a mile or so from the airport. There was no one else there, just a couple of sea lions basking on the seats in the shelter, almost as if they were waiting for a ferry too. Around us the most amazing birds were flying close by without a second glance at us. A dingy pulled up on the pontoon and in a surreal moment we stepped around a sea lion with her pup to get onto the inflatable that would take us to our boat.

When booking the holiday I had decided to spend more on the accommodation in the Amazon jungle and less on the boat to tour the Galapagos Isles. My phobia about reptiles, particularly snakes, meant I wanted to make sure we had somewhere substantial to sleep in at night in the jungle. Consequently the boat we booked for the Galapagos was pretty small and only slept twelve. It was old and cramped, but of all the holidays we have been on, I would love to go back there. From the moment we arrived it was magical, like no other place we had ever been. We had arrived at a small part of the world, underdeveloped, that is totally at peace with nature. It is no wonder they are called the enchanted Islands.

The Galapagos are made up of a series of islands scattered across a hundred or so miles in the Pacific Ocean. Each island is unique and starkly beautiful in its own way. Made famous by Charles Darwin and his discoveries about evolution, they are a protected nature reserve with strict codes of conduct to preserve the uninhibited wildlife. The benefit of this was that the birds and all the other creatures did not regard human beings as a threat and would carry on with their own business when you approached them.

On board we had an elderly French couple, an Italian couple and the rest of the group were younger European travellers, two guys, one Irish, one from Belgium and two girls from Holland. The French couple were a little alternative. The woman, whom we nicknamed 'Mae

West' wore as little clothing as possible both on the boat and on the island excursions and her husband sported only the tiniest pair of Speedos, that left absolutely nothing to the imagination, particularly when he sat with his legs wide apart. I am no prude, but this was a bit too much, Liz was embarrassed and Bart found the whole thing hilarious!

The Italian couple spoke little English and kept themselves very much to themselves. Dinner was the only time that this was an issue, as all the other guests would try to get seated on one of the two galley tables, just before the dinner bell was sounded, so that they didn't have to share with the two couples who had zero conversation. It became a bit of a game, with people jostling to sit ages before the food was served, just to sit on a table with people they could talk to.

On the second day we had sailed overnight and moored in a bay on Santa Cruz. We set off at 6.30 in the morning to see if we could find the famous sea turtle scrapes where they lay their eggs on the beach. The nature reserve rules do not permit smoking or any food to be taken onto the islands. This was made very clear from the outset, but, despite this, the French guy took food, lit up his pipe as he walked along the beach, strayed from the paths repeatedly and walked across one of the turtle scrapes. The couple had little respect for what they had come to see and quickly alienated themselves from the rest of the group. Things came to a bit of a head when they insisted to the guide that there was a third species of iguana on the islands and when our guide informed them there wasn't, they shouted at him and repeatedly called him stupid.

I was last up to dinner that evening and had the dubious pleasure of sitting between the French and Italian couple. The guys on the other table gave me a 'hard luck' look and I tried over the starter and the main course just to make a bit of light conversation. We got onto talking about cheese with the Italian couple, at which point the French man shrugged and said "What do the English know about cheese?" in French. As I had spent seven years selecting cheeses for my company, I probably knew far more than he did. I asked his wife to tell me what he had said and she suddenly reverted to French and pretended not to understand. I told her that her husband understood far more English than he let on. He continued to say rude things to me in French, most of which I got the gist of. By now the other table had gone quiet and Bart was giving me a mischievous grin as if to say 'I know you Mum and I know what's coming next'

When the husband finally finished mumbling insults about me I had had enough and I asked his wife to give her husband a message from me "Tell your husband he is very ignorant" I said, then got up and went to sit on the other table amid applause from the rest of the group. I wouldn't permit my son to behave like that even though some might make excuses for him and I certainly wouldn't tolerate that behaviour from someone who was probably old enough to be my father and should know better.

After that incident they kept to themselves, but on the second to last day I got a cracking picture of his wife. She was standing at the back of the boat, taking a photograph, with her skirt completely tucked in the back of her knickers. I zoomed in and got a great shot of her backside which went round to our fellow travellers via email when we returned to the UK!

Each island we visited was very different from the last. We saw blue footed boobies nesting, short eared owls hunting and the magnificent albatross breeding grounds. We walked along fine white sandy beaches amongst colonies of sea lions with day old pups suckling their mothers. We snorkelled in rocky bays and round the Devils crown rocks and watched as white-tip reef sharks swam beneath us. There was some form of wild life everywhere we went. The frigate bird followed us as our boat travelled between the islands, marine iguanas basked on the rocks between fishing expeditions and male sea lions lumbered across footpaths making their way to the 'bachelor' sleeping quarters for the night.

On our last evening we had dinner moored in a bay, before setting off to sail over night to Santa Cruz. Bart had made friends with the crew and travelling students and it was one of the first holidays I had felt able to relax and not keep one eye on him constantly. As the sun set, I watched as Bart made his way to the back of the boat and down onto the small platform that we used to board the dingy from. He was crouching down and I went to join him and see what had caught his attention. A young seal pup was swimming backwards and forwards underneath the boat and popping up for air in front of him. He held his hand down into the water and as it went by it rolled onto its back and exposed its tummy to him for a stroke. We sat for twenty minutes whilst the seal pup played with Bart and it was a precious experience, wondrous yet calming at the same time.

On the last morning we took small boats into the mangrove swamps and watched rays, over two feet wide, gliding through the shallow waters under the boat on their way back out to sea. There was also a group of seven white tip reef sharks in the shallow water, enjoying the warm lazy morning.

We said goodbye to the Galapagos and flew back to Quito later that morning. The next day we took a flight to Coca – a newly established town in the Amazon jungle. Although only a thirty five minute flight, we had flown over the Andes and dropped down into a much hotter and humid climate. We were met at the airport and travelled by jeep to the river where we waited for our boat, at which point Bart realised he had forgotten his boots and we had to wait while someone returned to the airport to collect them.

Although over a thousand miles from the sea, the river was amazingly wide in some places and shallow in some places with wide mud and sand banks that a boat could easily go aground on. The journey took over two hours and we travelled in a long thin boat with a powerful outboard motor. Every once in a while we passed large ships moored up against clearings in the forest. The guide explained these were oil fields and that oil was Ecuador's second income revenue – which is a problem as it's estimated that reserves will run out in around thirty years. Bart and I had done a homework project on the river Amazon and we were both fascinated to see it and its sheer size.

After a couple of hours travelling upstream, we switched boats at a narrow tributary and climbed into a hollowed out tree trunk with tiny seats and paddles. The boat sat seven in line, which was handy as there were four of us plus an American biologist, the guide and a couple of young men with paddles. We started our journey down a narrow river no wider than twenty feet in places. The water was the colour of tea without milk and the vast trees joined together over our heads. Though Bart was generally sensible and far less impulsive now, I had a quiet word with him along the lines of "Don't rock the boat", quite literally!

A journey that should have taken half an hour took nearly an hour and a half. After only five minutes our guide had spotted a small anaconda which luckily I missed and after that we all had our binoculars out spotting birds, insects and monkeys on the way. Eventually the small river opened out into a large lake and there on the far side was the Napa Valley Nature Reserve. As we approached the wooden quay jutting out into the lake, our enthusiastic guide said we could snorkel in the lake. Bart was all for it! Our new friend, the biologist, asked what sort of wild life was in there and our guide replied "Anaconda, caiman, stingrays and piranha". That for me was the end of the snorkelling discussion!

The sun was setting as we were shown to our idyllic thatched bungalows right on the waters' edge. Liz and I shared one and Robert and Bart were in the one next door. We changed quickly for dinner and made our way through the beautiful gardens to the restaurant. The sun had set quickly and only small lights lit the way. After dinner I realised I had forgotten something from the room and after ten minutes of unsuccessfully trying to bribe Bart to go for me, I set off on my own.

I was on a heightened state of alert that I might see a snake and my fears were verified when I glanced down and saw something yellow and black slithering along the path in front of me. I screamed a yelp and stood dead still watching. It was very long and thin and it took me a few moments to realise it was an army of giant ants carrying pieces of leaf foliage on their backs!

The next morning it rained heavily. We went down to the boat house to get kitted out in wellingtons and then set off to visit a village to meet the locals and see how they lived. The highlight was an audience with the local Shaman. He was supposed to have special magical powers to drive away demons and bad thoughts. Nobody wanted to volunteer but Bart stepped forward to be put under his spell and I watched as we sat in a ring around him. The Shaman hummed, then moved and waved his hands constantly over Bart's head. Any fears I had were dispatched when Bart looked at us, grinned and pulled his best Mr Bean face! He said he felt much calmer after the experience and he was indeed calm for the next hour or so – but we are not sure what impact Bart had on the Shaman, and joked about it for the rest of the holiday.

The next morning we took a boat ride to the other end of the lake. By now the family had agreed to share the paddling with the locals and after much splashing and crashing of paddles, we arrived at our destination. Getting into and out of the boat was a challenge as there were no wooden landing platforms, just a red clay river bank, which was quite steep and slippery in places. We scrambled up onto the path and set off on a walk to an observation tower. Bart had an aggravating habit of swinging some of the lower branches as he passed. He wouldn't listen to my warnings, but did take note when the guide advised him that something unpleasant might drop down from above. The very thought made my blood run cold.

We walked for about half an hour until we reached the observation platform which was built at the top of a tree eighty metres from the ground. To get to it you had to climb up a metal framed staircase and then cross a narrow gangway before climbing onto the relative safety of the wooden platform. I was concerned for Bart, but equally anxious for myself and Liz as neither of us has a head for heights. I needn't have worried about Bart; he had rushed up the steps two or three at a time and nimbly negotiated the rickety gang plank. Liz and I took quite a bit more time and only reached the platform after words of encouragement and hands out stretched from either side. The forest was shrouded in mist to begin with and I wondered why we had risked life and limb to reach this vantage point, but as the sun rose the mist cleared and we had a wonderful panoramic view of the forest canopy.

We spotted monkeys, a sloth and an incredible variety of birds, but after two hours the heat and the insect life was getting to Liz and I so we made our way down to the shelter of the forest floor. Bart started his descent a few minutes later preceded by a flow of water which he gleefully announced was his wee! But it turned out that he had emptied the last of his water bottle on us. At least that was what he told us!

We took various guided trips into the reserve and one afternoon Robert and I decided to go on a walk with Mike the marine biologist and our guides, whilst Bart and Liz stayed behind and lazed around. Bart seemed to be much steadier these days and he and Liz were arguing a lot less. We paddled across the lake and clambered from the canoe onto a rough path. After a few yards, the guide stopped and inspected some droppings and announced it was fresh puma poo. Great! Snakes and caiman to worry about and now a large wild cat – lucky, I thought, I am not afraid of spiders!

It was around four in the afternoon and still very hot. We had been walking for about an hour when Mike said he wasn't feeling too good and asked if I had any sweets on me. He said he was a 'part-time diabetic' and hadn't had any problems for six months, but it was clear he was in a bad way. Luckily the guide had some biscuits on him and we stopped while he recovered and the guide wandered off into the undergrowth wielding his machete – what had he seen? He returned a few moments later with a fan he had cut for me from a huge leaf and I breathed a sigh of relief. We walked on for another hour or more before finally coming to a small river where the canoe was waiting.

The second part of the tour was caiman spotting. As we paddled down the narrow river the guides pointed out a caiman basking in the dying sunlight. I fixed my binoculars on it and adjusted them as we approached. When it no longer fitted in the lenses I took the binoculars away and realised it was only about one metre long. I chuckled; my vivid imagination had played tricks on me. In my mind it was several metres long and nearly as wide.

The river opened out onto the lake and we spent a while looking for caiman on the shoreline, with the aid of a torch, as darkness fell. I felt relatively safe in the boat and congratulated myself on overcoming my reptile phobia as we paddled back towards dinner. It was pitch black now and we could see the lights of our accommodation twinkling. I was sitting quietly in the back of the boat when there was a huge splash and the boat rocked precariously from side to side, nearly capsizing. There were shouts and the torch flashed across the lake illuminating a three metre long caiman. I had thought the boys were just larking around at the front of the boat but the close proximity of this large reptile shook me and suddenly I was quite pleased that we were leaving the following day.

We reached safety and met up with Bart and Liz in the bar. Before dinner we chatted to the lodge director. I enquired about the helicopters that flew quite low nearby and asked him if they belonged to the local oil companies. He laughed and said we were close to the Colombian border and they were troops out looking for drug runners as it was the season. How naïve can you be?

Liz and I didn't sleep well that night. It was extremely humid and there was a wild electric storm. There seemed to be lots of strange noises coming from outside our hut and when the rain finally came, in the early hours of the morning, it was so noisy that sleep was out of the question.

There was a dead piranha fish at the foot of our hut

steps and as we left the reserve that morning in heavy rain I was pleased to be leaving. Yet every so often I wish I was back there, amidst the amazing bird and insect life and the dangerous beauty of the jungle.

Chapter 30

A Boy Amongst Men

That September Liz started her degree at university studying criminology and Bart started a course in aerospace engineering. He hadn't wanted to know his GCSE results whilst we were away and an envelope, addressed to him, was sitting in the pile of post on our return. He opened it and wandered off alone to read the results and then returned with a huge bashful smile on his face. He had passed his eight GCSEs including a C grade in double science – higher grade!

The previous spring we had debated long and hard what college and which subjects Bart was going to do. He had started to show a keen interest in training to be an airline pilot and we had been invited to one of the country's leading training establishments for the opening of their second flight simulator. I had taken the day off work and Rob, Bart and I had driven up for the occasion.

When we arrived we were escorted by mature students all wearing the smart uniform of the college. We were given a tour of the facilities and trainee pilots demonstrated the various flight training equipment. We queued with other would-be pilots who had come along for the day. Bart was a boy amongst men. The flight simulation took about ten minutes and was set to automatic. As the 'cockpit' only took six or eight people the queues moved slowly and we hung around for nearly an hour before we got to see inside. The two airline crew who queued with us gave the simulator a cursory glance then left us behind with one of the instructors.

Bart was fascinated and asked if he could sit in the pilot's seat. The instructor encouraged him and started to fiddle with various knobs before standing back and asking Bart if he would like to fly it? Bart didn't need a second invitation and we set off down the runway of Gatwick airport, part on the grass, part on the runway, whilst Bart came to terms with the controls. He had a computer flight simulator at home, but it was controlled only by a joy stick. This simulator was exactly like a Boeing 737 and had all of the controls of a real plane.

The instructor guided Bart and we took off to the West and made a turn along the North Downs. I had done this flight so many times on business I knew exactly where we were. He flew for twenty minutes before he came round and started his descent into Gatwick again. A man and his wife joined us in the simulator, she made a comment about coming in too steeply and her husband cut across her to say Bart was doing rather well. We landed quite neatly, without crashing, and Bart released the controls from his now, rather sweaty hands.

The instructor asked him how old he was and when

Bart replied that he was just fifteen the instructor patted him on the back and told him he should seriously consider training to become a pilot, as he seemed to have a natural talent. But first Bart needed to finish his secondary education.

The air training college encouraged its applicants to have three A-levels, two in sciences and one in maths. Our first choice was for Bart to go on to the local further education college which had a reputation for their good pass grades. We had visited the college and I was quite impressed but Bart was less certain. The college required students to take a minimum of four subjects. Bart felt, and I secretly agreed, that this would over stretch him academically. We had had some pretty big arguments in the spring, when Bart already felt over faced with the number of GCSE's he was taking. I agreed with him and I knew, working full time, I couldn't help him to stay focused on so much work, but I was not aware of any alternatives and I could see his opportunity to train to be a pilot slipping away from him before he had even started. A careers advisor came to the rescue and told Bart about a course, running at a different college, on aerospace engineering. We went to the interview and Bart was conditionally accepted, depending on his GCSE grades.

The college was a lot more relaxed than our first choice and it was less academic and prestigious, but it offered a very practical subject that would hold Bart's interest far more than straight academic A level subjects.

Chapter 31

Life at College

The first week Bart started college I tried to establish who his principal lecturer was, and talk to him about his ADHD. Because De Leeds didn't have a sixth form, Bart had no alternative but to change to another college for further education, and he lost his educational statement that entitled him to help with learning.

If De Leeds had offered a sixth form and Bart had stayed on he would still have been entitled to this help. It was bureaucratic nonsense but Bart had matured a lot over the months and I explained the situation to his new college and asked them if some help might be forthcoming – even if we had to pay for it.

As was usual with Bart's education, none of the people I spoke to at the college really had any idea what ADHD was and the most I could secure from them was a promise that they would keep an eye on Bart's progress and let me know if he was struggling at all.

Bart started to attend lectures and within two weeks it was clear to me, but not to the college, that he was experiencing difficulties. The year group had thirty students and one of the lecturers informed me that they usually like around fifteen in a class. The higher the number of pupils, the less one to one experience they had with the lecturers.

The course had attracted a high percentage of students aged sixteen to eighteen who either saw it as a 'cushy number' compared to straight A-levels, or had been 'encouraged' to leave their previous school due to their lack of personal commitment to their education. In short the group was double the size it should have been with a lot of disruptive elements in it.

Bart's biggest problem was staying tuned in and focussed during lectures and the constant disruption and interruption made it difficult for him to sustain his attention. Ironically the disruptive behaviour that Bart had meted out in classrooms gone by was coming home to roost from those around him. After a few more weeks I realised Bart was falling behind. He found the subject matter challenging, he lost concentration in lectures and if he asked a question some of the lads started to take the mickey.

As the weeks went by Bart became quite withdrawn. He stopped wanting to go to college and he lost interest in what he was studying. By Christmas it all came to a head and Bart announced he didn't want to continue with the course. He, amongst others, was being bullied, called names and generally the butt for all jokes. A couple of the lads had threatened violence and I was probably more scared for Bart's well being than I had ever been.

I contacted Walter, Bart's old head of special needs, and asked him if he would be prepared to attend a meeting at the college with me for support. I had had several conversations with the college and I wasn't happy that they were taking Bart's learning difficulty or the bullying seriously and I asked to have a meeting with the key stake holders.

The Sunday before the meeting, Bart and I went for a drive in the car, parked in a beauty spot and sat and chatted about his feelings and what he wanted to do. His self-esteem and self-worth were on the floor, his confidence in his ability to do the course work was zero and his self motivation was understandably poor. I felt so sad for Bart that he was so unhappy that he just wanted to give it all up. I felt angry with the bullies who seemed to have won. I felt frustrated that after the long journey we had come on together, Bart was so disheartened that he just wanted to walk away from it all and I worried what the future held for Bart if he didn't gain any qualifications.

The dream to become a pilot was his, not mine. I was only there to support him to achieve his dreams but I felt that his dreams were slipping away from him and I feared for what might become of him, just as I had done when he was a little boy. We sat for some time in silence and then I asked him gently if we could sit down at home and make a list of the good and bad bits of life at the moment. Bart agreed and when we got home we put down on paper all the things that seemed to be against him and what he had going for him. The bad outweighed the good by two to one, but it gave us a starting point. On the next page we wrote possible solutions to the problems and we scoped out the choices that Bart faced. In the end it all boiled down to stand up and face the situation or walk away and wonder what might have been.

225

The following week Bart, Rob, Walter and I all piled into the car and drove to the college for our meeting. They had rustled up five attendees including the course manager and a special needs manager who had been looking into Bart's case. The meeting was held in a tiny office with nine of us all sitting on top of each other. After introductions, I took the lead in the meeting and I decided to share what Bart and I had written the previous weekend. It made sad reading but I pushed on and asked what the college planned to do to support Bart's ADHD and specifically what they planned to do about the bullying. Bart was far from perfect, but he deserved the best possible chance like any other pupil.

Taking Walter to the meeting was a good move. Nobody knew he was coming and they didn't know his agenda. It added a bit more gravity to our presence and an outsider's professional guidance. He didn't say much but his quiet, authoritative presence seemed to act like a silent reminder that this situation needed to be dealt with professionally.

The college's special needs representative had made a comment earlier in the meeting that the prospect of Bart becoming a pilot was unrealistic. I chose to let that comment go as we had bigger issues to discuss but, towards the end of the meeting he said again there was little chance of Bart becoming a pilot. I stopped the conversation, looked him fully in the eye and told him that it was not his place to make that statement. He replied that it was true and I again told him he was not qualified to make such a statement. He said little for the rest of the meeting and at the end the college came up with a plan of additional one to one support for Bart with extra tuition and assurances that the bullies would be seen and dealt with.

Rome wasn't built in a day, but gradually the situation improved and Bart got back on track with his coursework. By the end of the year only thirteen pupils passed to go onto the second year and many of the troublemakers were amongst the ones that didn't return.

During my own career I have faced intimidation and bullying and helped other colleagues who were in a similar situation. I have come to the conclusion that people bully and intimidate for two main reasons. Either, you have something that they want and they are jealous, or you are good at what you do and they feel threatened. Either way it's bad news if you are on the receiving end of it and I was glad that, because I had experienced it first hand, I was able to help Bart put it into some perspective.

Walter didn't need to help us, but he did. On the way home from the meeting he talked quietly to Bart about a similar incident that had happened to him early in life. He spoke about how he felt and how he had overcome it and gone on to exceed in sport, where he had been a member of the British Olympics team for some years. Walter was a slightly built man, but he had great presence and a voice of authority that just couldn't be ignored.

He continued to support Bart through the Winter. He visited our home and sat in front of the log fire in our hall, quietly reassuring Bart that things would be OK. Bart responded well to this outside help. Part of being a good parent is recognising your own limitations of influence and requesting and accepting help from outside when it is needed. There is no place for pride and with Walter's help, Bart went back to college even more determined to succeed.

Chapter 32

Let Muse-ic be the Spice of Life

I was bought up with a broad taste in music. My father loved classical music and an early exposure to it had resulted in me being as happy with the strains of classical music in the house as I was with modern rock and pop. When Liz and Bart were ten and twelve we took them to a classical FM concert at the Albert Hall. Most of the tickets were sold out by the time I got to hear about it and we ended up sitting in the choir stalls which are up behind the orchestra.

The concert was being broadcast on radio simultaneously and I wondered if Bart would find a means to make his voice heard, so I didn't mention the live broadcast and we got through the concert with no incidents of burping or pig noises. It would have been just too tempting for him had he known!

As Bart reached his early teens, he started to leave classical FM radio on when he went to sleep, very quietly, so it just broke the silence of the night. He said he found it a calming influence, particularly when he couldn't sleep, which makes a lot of sense.

Probably, like most generations, I considered that growing up in the 60's and 70's was the most exciting time in the development of pop and rock music. The Beatles, The Stones, The Who, Pink Floyd etcetera were all bands I enjoyed, so when Roger Walters and the Who announced they were appearing in Hyde Park I made sure that I got the family tickets. We didn't limit ourselves to one era and saw REM, Elton John and Keane a few times, but our absolute favourite was a band called Muse. Though much heavier than some of the other bands, the lyrics from their songs are amazing and certain songs have been poignant in mirroring our family circumstances and emotions.

Muse at Wembley was the first big concert that Bart, Liz and I went to, along with 90,000 other people. We almost missed the start of the concert when Bart went missing, last seen going to the gents. Wembley is huge and I was worried we had missed each other as Liz and I had gone off to buy drinks. But just when I was slipping into low level panic mode and asking a steward to search the toilets, Bart emerged. He informed us that the queue for the cubicle loos' was forever as blokes were smoking wacky-backy in them rather than using them for their principle intended purpose.

Liz was adept at worming her way through the crowds to get to the front, rather like the artful dodger, and Bart and I trundled behind feeling a bit embarrassed. This is a tactic that we have used in most gigs, send the pretty one out in front, and the rest of the family follow!

We made it about two thirds of the way down the pitch with a great view. The acoustics were excellent and the band's performance was amazing. Bart was at that slightly self-conscious 'Kevin' stage so he stood a little way from Liz and I whilst we sang and bounced up and down to the songs.

The following year we saw Muse twice, at the Albert Hall and just outside Dublin. The Irish trip was a completely impulsive folly on my part. All the tickets for the UK venues were sold out, but some were still available for Marleigh Park. In a moment of madness, I logged on, bought the tickets, bought four return flights for £10 each and booked a hotel in central Dublin.

Life, as a hectic working mum, was about treats. I sometimes felt so tired and stressed with the pressures of work and family that I doubted I would survive the frantic pace I lived. My compensation became wacky treats, like an unusual holiday, a night in a castle or a trip to a gig. I liked to surprise the family, telling them that if I told them all that I knew, I would have to kill them! Only joking, of course, but my unpredictability did keep them guessing.

The trip over to Dublin was fine and the hotel was adequate. We wandered through the streets of Dublin that afternoon and had a late lunch in a small Italian restaurant. Around 6 pm we got ready to go off to the concert and Robert settled down with a few lagers to watch some of the Olympics on TV. The trip out of town seemed to last forever in the evening traffic and we walked the last mile as the roads had been closed by the police. The venue seemed to be little more than a field with a stage in it, but the crowd were a friendly bunch and, with Liz in the lead, we were able to get about thirty feet from the stage.

Kasabian were the supporting band and during their performance the guy in front of me asked if I had a light. Happy to oblige, I lent him my lighter. Within seconds the whiff of wacky-backy hit our nostrils. Bart, Liz and several of the crowd tutted at me for giving them a light – but how was I to know?

As with Wembley, the band was amazing and people high as kites crowd-surfed over our heads to get to the front. When the last song had been played and the applause and whistles died away we made our way out of the ground. The three of us stopped briefly to form a human shield around a couple who had fallen over as, with that number of people in the crowd, it would have been easy to get trampled. We asked them if they were OK and when the girl looked up, with pupils as large as saucers, we realised they were both stoned and probably wouldn't feel anything if a herd of elephants trampled across them!

On the way out to Marleigh Park the cab driver had said we would easily pick one up for the return journey to Dublin but, of course, the roads were shut with lots of police and no sign of a bus, let alone a cab. We walked a good three miles before eventually flagging a cab down. It didn't matter though, we had a great evening with an amazing band and even getting up at 5.30 the following morning to take the first plane back to work couldn't take anything away from the experience.

Chapter 33

Outside Interests

Bart had given up air cadets when the pressure of GCSEs had taken up too much of his time. The following year he joined a local marine cadet company and went two nights a week. He got to go to camp and had a great time escaping and capturing fellow cadets. Because Bart was still forgetful, I was less than impressed when he announced he was going away for a rifle shooting weekend when I had planned a family weekend away. But part of growing up is pursuing the things that interest you, so Bart set off for a couple of days rifle shooting and Liz, Rob and I went for a relaxing weekend at a spa.

We had a great time swimming and being pampered and Bart had a great time shooting, but he only got the chance to fire twenty rounds each day. Because Bart had previously done archery he seemed to be quite good with a rifle and he was picked to go away to Lincolnshire to practise, with the possibility of qualifying to shoot in the annual competition at Bisley.

He set off on the Thursday and the first couple of nights he was away we got short 'phone calls to say he was doing OK with his shooting and the food was OK but not enough. Bart thought that he was only away for three days and then coming home before possibly going to Bisley the following weekend. But something had got lost in the translation and he was in fact away for ten days. After five days in Lincolnshire Bart had had enough. Some joker had hidden his boots, he hadn't packed enough civilian clothes and he was fed up.

He texted me, early one morning whilst I was on the bus going to work and asked "How soon after a death do you have a funeral?" Bart was obviously scraping the barrel for an excuse to return home, but I thought he might regret it if he gave up so I texted back and told him it was only a couple of days until he transferred to Bisley and to use his shooting as a means of levelling the scores. He stuck with it and he and about eight hundred other cadets made their way to Bisley for the start of the competition on the Friday.

Bart negotiated one caveat for staying – could we drop some more clothes off for him? So Robert set off for Bisley with a carrier bag with Bart's clothes in.

Bisley is a big camp and Roberts's first problem was getting in through the security gate with no pass. He had just been advised that he couldn't gain access or leave the bag when a Gurkha soldier offered to take him in his military truck round the camp in search of Lima Company. Eventually they turned up at a hut and Robert entered a room with a load of senior military personnel with lots of 'scrambled egg' on their shoulders. He felt a complete goon as he held the carrier bag and explained that it contained his son's clothes. The major he addressed managed to keep a straight face whilst assuring Rob that the bag would get to Bart, but several of the majors hid smiles of amusement which did nothing to make him feel less ridiculous.

Bart 'phoned later in the day to say he was shooting well, and thank us for the clothes. He also said that his slightly AD Dad had sent him a pair of his own jeans and not Bart's! "It's the thought that counts son" I replied and we ended the conversation having a chuckle at his father's forgetfulness.

On the Saturday morning I got a text "I'm shooting well" and in the afternoon he 'phoned and babbled on about something called the 'dream team' which there was a slim chance he might get picked for. I was looking forward to seeing him the next day and hearing all about his experiences and I paid little attention to mention of the following days activities.

The Sunday morning Liz and I rode out in the countryside on a beautiful sunny day. We were about six miles from home and had just stopped for a drink in a country pub when my mobile rang. It was Bart. He told me that he had been picked for the dream team and that he was shooting well. I was really pleased for him and glad he had stuck it out in Lincolnshire.

Later that day I drove to pick him up and by the time I got there the rest of the company had gone leaving just Bart, the sergeant and one other cadet. Bart was grinning from ear to ear and bouncing something up and down in his hand. "Here, catch mum", he said and lobbed it to me. Luckily I caught it. In my hand I held the gold medal for winning the entire competition! It was a sweet moment for Bart and for me and as we drove home belting out Muse's song Knights of Cydonia

– "No one's going to take me alive..." I reflected on where we had come from and what Bart had achieved.

Just for a laugh, the week before Bart went to Lincolnshire, he had told one of the other students that he was going to shoot at Bisley. The other guy had laughed in his face and told him it was rubbish. Pissed off, Bart had said that not only was he going to Bisley, he was going to win. He only said that to retaliate, not because he thought for a moment that he would. But Bart had won and it was another notch up in his self-esteem.

Chapter 34

Driving Me Round the Bend!

Bart was seventeen in June and his first driving lesson was at 10 o'clock that morning. Over the previous months Rob and I had driven to a local disused airfield and allowed Bart to sit behind the wheel and go through the basics. This wasn't about turning him into Jenson Button, but more about adapting to change. When Bart faced change he could act unpredictably and this was when accidents were most likely to happen. Rather than waiting for Bart's seventeenth birthday, we decided to let him acclimatise to the prospect of driving.

I think most parents feel some concern when their children become old enough to drive. They are suddenly alone and no longer under your parental supervision. It's not a coincidence that insurance for newly qualified teenagers, particularly male, is so high – the accidents and claims speak for themselves. By permitting Bart to practise, we were able to instil some basic ground rules into him.

On his first official lesson, Bart started the car up and drove off with his instructor, having posed for the usual family album mug shots with his best Mr Bean smile! He wasn't driven to a quiet cul-de-sac like his sister; he just got in and drove. During the time he was taking lessons we would take him out for practise. I tended to use this as a treat, after his homework was completed. This reward system helped to keep Bart on target with his college work and gave him valuable experience to make him a more experienced driver when he had passed his test.

All of the practise paid off and Bart passed his test first time. I was proud of him, but in the back of my mind was a niggling doubt. Would Bart start to display impulsive behaviour when he was out alone? This son of ours had gone from the fidgety naughty boy outside the class room to a young man behind the wheel of a vehicle that could take lives if not handled properly. I will admit we had a couple of incidents that have scared me, but far less than when his sister first qualified and I had a permanent aching bum from tensing myself when she drove! Overall Bart is a natural, positive and responsible driver that I feel very relaxed with.

The only occasion when I didn't feel so relaxed was the first Christmas after he passed his test. The weather forecasters had predicted snow and they were not wrong. Most of the country ground to a halt and we were virtually snowed in with the nearby motorway closed. I had gone to check the horses early that evening and had got into a skid just two hundred yards from home. I regard myself as a pretty sensible and capable driver and I was not amused when I got home and found a row had broken out about whether Bart could drive his car in the snow that evening. For me it was a no brainer – it was the sort of evening that you didn't drive unless your life depended on it. Bart, however, had other ideas. He loved the snow and wanted to experience the challenge of driving in it.

Wisely, Robert had hidden his car keys, but this had flipped Bart into a blind rage and by the time I got home a painting was damaged and the drawer in the office was broken and testosterone levels were at an all time high. Not for the first time I stood between them both and told them to back off. The problem was that I could understand Bart's desire to experience what it was like to drive in the snow, but his aggressive behaviour was clearly not the way to go about things. We had always worked on the premise of rewarding good behaviour and withdrawing rewards for poor behaviour. Whilst Bart hadn't lost his temper for over a year, this was a major tantrum and whilst in this frame of mind he was not fit to take a car on the road.

I've learnt over the years that the art of good negotiation is to know when to give a little and what to give. I decided to take Bart out in my car if he calmed down. His father was understandably angry about Bart's outburst, but the two of them together in this frame of mind was a volatile mix and I asked Robert to stop communicating or acknowledging anything Bart said. This 'moving away' technique was useful as it diffused the situation, rather than inflaming it. Bart marched outside in a fury and I followed, which suited me as I still had warm layers of clothing on from my trip to the horse. Bart, on the other hand, was only wearing a thin T-shirt with jeans and the minus zero temperature soon started to cool him down. After what seemed like ages, but was probably only twenty minutes Bart was calm enough to go back inside to apologise and I offered him a ride in my car. Robert looked at me nonplussed, but this was the pact I had made with myself. My car had ABS braking and a decent amount of protection around it, whereas Bart's thirteen year old mini would not be a sensible option.

Before we set off I told Bart any damage to my car would come out of his savings and I deliberately chose a steep narrow road that goes up onto the downs. My objective was to prove that the roads were impassable and treacherous and maybe scare him a bit (foolish really when I reflect on this). We started the steep climb and only managed one hundred yards before I had to admit defeat. By now Bart and I were back to talking normally to each other and, as I slid backwards down the hill, I concentrated on trying not to slide into the steep banks on either side of the narrow road, Bart asked if the car would go uphill better backwards? This was typical of Bart, you had just had a blazing row, you were stuck in a very awkward predicament and then he would ask one of his 'what if?' questions that I couldn't answer.

Bart backed the car down the rest of the hill for me and performed a perfect one hundred and eighty degree turn on the snow and ice. There were no other cars about as the road was officially closed, so for some reason best known only to myself, I let Bart have a go at backing my car up the hill. We gave up after a few minutes, with the smell of burning rubber and a slipping handbrake.

When we got home I asked Bart if he had something to say to me. He said "sorry" and I was surprised as I was actually looking for a 'Thank you". I told him to go inside and apologise to Liz and his Dad and bring out the mini keys. With his father shaking his head in disapproval and a few gulps of wine inside me, we set off again in the snow. I did this because Bart had calmed. He had made his peace with the family and he had also handled my car very well. He and I were friends again and having got a feel for driving in the snow, I thought it would be good to build on this experience before the snow disappeared in a couple of days or I lost my nerve! Some might say I was irresponsible to let Bart drive in those conditions, but the condition of the mind is the most important – if that is right, then we can cope with the conditions outside us.

It was an Interesting drive, with a capital "I". I was allowed to smoke in the car with the window right down, a privilege not usually granted. Bart attempted to get to the top of the downs in reverse and after thirty minutes of sliding and revving we achieved this. We drove, sliding and slithering, along the ridge of the downs for a few miles until we came to what is arguably one of the steepest roads that leads back off the downs and towards home. "Shall I?" Bart asked, "Why not son" I replied and off we set.

Bart took the first part very slowly; he was quiet, intent on not hitting the bank, or worse still, going over the side. Two thirds of the way down is a sharp dog leg bend to the left, which we glided round sideways. His one impulsive act was a hand brake turn as we neared the bottom and the road went under the motorway. The motorway bridge wall came rapidly towards me as the car spun, then receded as Bart took control of the car and drove out of the skid. Tight lipped I suggested it was time for home – this cocky action had made me nearly wet myself and was both unnecessary and typical.

A few nights later I reflected on Bart's driving skills and told him that, despite the heart stopping hand brake turn, he had in fact handled the car superbly in the icy conditions. Bart grinned back at me sheepishly. He asked me if I remembered him taking the first part of the hill so slowly. "Yes" I replied. "Well actually Mum, I wasn't driving, we were just sliding, I thought you could hear the engine Mum, I thought you knew!" Well thankfully I hadn't known or I might have chosen to evacuate and take my chances. What is interesting though is the honesty between us, and honesty is a valuable commodity. If you can be honest with each other then you can both learn from each other.

Chapter 35

Bart's Future

Bart was seventeen and a half, when he applied to the flying college that we had visited a couple of years before. It was still his dream to become a pilot, though Lord knows how we would finance it. Bart applied to attend a two day assessment course to see if he had the necessary social, practical and academic skills to train as a pilot.

One Friday morning a letter addressed to Bart plopped through the letterbox and onto the mat. Bart returned from college that evening and was delighted to read that his assessment was the Wednesday and Thursday of the following week. This allowed little time for preparation and no time to get anxious – just take it as it came.

I was nervous about Bart driving one hundred and fifty miles to the college at five in the morning. It was winter and it would be dark until at least seven. He hadn't driven on a motorway in the dark before and the rush hour traffic was an endless stream around London at that time in the morning. I was also aware that his mini would offer him little protection if he was involved in a prang, so after a couple of rows we agreed to drive there together and I would catch a train back into town for work.

Five a.m. that Wednesday morning Bart and I were wandering round the kitchen in a sleepy state, trying to make a cup of tea and wake ourselves up for the drive ahead. Bart dressed in jeans for the drive, picked up his overnight holdall and went out to get the car started. I got my computer and briefcase together and took one last look round the kitchen before we left. Bart came to the kitchen door, urging me to get a move on. "Have you got everything Bart?" I asked, "Yes Mum, it's all in the car", Bart looked at me and followed my eyes to the cooker where his suit and tie were hanging. He picked it up and grinned, "Well almost" he said.

The journey round the M25 was slow. There was loads of traffic and it was dark and raining. The mini objected to speeds over 60 mph so we sat in the slow lane, sandwiched between lorries and listened to the radio as we made slow progress. When we were thirty miles from the college, Absolute radio played Muse Starlight and I found a service station on the motorway where we could stop for a coffee and Bart could change.

On business I had stopped at this service station many times and as Bart was obviously nervous, clutching his suit, I guided him towards the disabled toilets, so he would have room to change. He pulled a Mr Bean face and said something funny as he shut the door. Chuckling I walked on towards the ladies. "Where are you going?" a guy coming towards me asked. "To the ladies" I replied. "Not in here you're not!" he said and I looked up to see I had just walked into the gents' toilet. Embarrassed, I turned on my heel and found my way to the ladies. Then I bought coffee and orange juice and sat waiting for Bart to appear.

I watched as Bart walked towards me in his suit and tie. He looked like a suave, sophisticated young man and a thousand miles removed from the skinny little boy who had caused so much disruption to anyone he came into contact with for all those years. Guys glanced at him and a couple of attractive girls openly eyed him up. At that point I was the proudest and happiest mum in the world. I didn't care how he got on in his interview, it just mattered that we had got here, to this point in life, where I could see Bart had a good future, whatever that might be.

He elected to drive the last few miles and I was content to sip my coffee and relax. We had agreed that he would drop me at the station, then head on to the college alone, but finding the station was proving a problem. It was shown on a map but there were no signs for it. In frustration we stopped and asked a poor guy who had a slight speech impediment and a very broad country accent. After three attempts the basic gist of it was there was no station, but I could get a bus into town.

Bart found his way round the one way system and dropped me at the bus stop. I felt mixed emotions and tears pricked at my eyes as he went to drive off. He must have read my face, as he rolled down his window and shouted out "Bye bye darling, you can go now. I don't need you anymore" in his best Bubbles Devere impersonation from Little Britain. Bart's sense of humour always brought a smile to my face and brightened my day. I hopped onto the bus in an optimistic frame of mind and when it finally terminated in the town centre, I walked down to the station and caught a fast train to Paddington a few minutes later.

All that day I felt nervous for Bart. He was moving into a man's world and for the next couple of days he would be mixing with a very different calibre of people than he was previously used to. I wasn't sure what I thought about his potential to become a pilot. Bart would probably be the youngest applicant and I guessed that they would put him through the assessment and then say "Thank you very much. Go out and get some of life's experiences and come back in a couple of years when you are a bit more mature".

That evening Bart 'phoned to tell me how the day had gone. He and the rest of the group had sat maths and physics tests and he had had a go in a flight simulator, but not the big one he had flown previously. He reckoned that overall the day had gone OK and two guys on the course were also staying at the same hotel as him, so they were popping out for a drink together. I warned Bart to get an early night, not to drink and drive, then said goodnight and hung up.

The next day I was in work just after 7 am as usual, and I spent the whole day in meetings about Christmas, which kept me focussed. I looked up the times of the return trains and settled on the 5.15 from Paddington. The train ran late and I told Bart that I would catch the bus and meet him where he had left me the previous morning.

Feeling a bit nervous about the outcome of Bart's assessment, I decided to make a pit stop at the ladies in the station and walking towards the door I noticed a 'male cleaner' board in front of the door. Male cleaners didn't bother me so I marched through the double doors to find two guys in the loo. It was only milliseconds before I assessed the equipment and realised I had walked into another gents' toilet! This was starting to become a habit. I retraced my steps in front of a packed railway concourse and reflected this sort of thing could happen to anyone!

Undeterred I made my way up the high street to the bus stop and set off to meet Bart. He 'phoned me when I was about ten minutes away and asked me to stay on the bus until it got to the airport where he would pick me up. Fifteen minutes later we were in the car, Bart was driving and we were heading for London. The miles whizzed by as Bart told me all about the last two days, the team building exercise and his final interview. When he had finished his account I still wasn't sure how he had done.

We stopped at the same service station and Bart remained in the car and explained to me that he had passed all the entry tests with the exception of maths. You needed twenty eight points to get into the college and he had twenty five, but he had been invited to go back to the college and re sit the maths test. I was jumping for joy and incredibly proud of Bart's achievement. To get this far in the process at his age was a credit to him.

Bart finished his aerospace engineering course and did well with his grades. He took the summer off and learnt to glide in between studying for his maths retake. A different man was emerging from the boy. I no longer had to goad him into studying. He seemed to grow up that summer. I had recently retired from my job and it was a joy to be around him and Liz in those long summer months. Bart and I knocked down a wall to make one large room out of two tiny ones and I still remember seeing his eye ball through the first tiny hole, as we looked at each other from opposite sides of the wall!

The recreation and peace Bart found in learning to glide paid dividends and he took his first solo flight that September. Thankfully I was blissfully unaware that he was doing so until he arrived home that evening with a big grin on his face and a video clip on his phone, taken somewhere high above the airfield.

That October Bart returned to the Aviation College and re-sat his maths test. We drove up together one Friday and after collecting a coffee and a muffin from the service station, Bart left me sitting in the car whilst he went off to find his examiner. I flicked through D.I.Y. books but found it hard to focus on anything; these next few hours would determine his future.

Two hours later, Bart emerged and walked across the car park to me. He was avoiding my gaze as he knew his eyes could not hide the result from me. He climbed nonchalantly into the car and sat a full few minutes in silence before he passed me the certificate that confirmed he had been successful. A huge grin spread across his face as he looked through the paperwork that invited him to train to be a commercial first officer. He went through his scores and the comments from the interview after the tests. Bart had raised his original score from twenty five points to thirty six – he had done very well.

That weekend we celebrated with friends at home as the news started to sink in and we enjoyed those last few weeks before he left home to start his course. I could never have dreamed we would come to this and I am sure that many of Bart's junior school teachers would have a job getting their head around it too!

Before Bart was three, I realized he was different from some of the other kids but I worked with him and stuck by him. When he was in primary school, undiagnosed, I sheltered and defended his actions. In junior school I fought for him and in secondary school I was his champion. I never gave up on Bart and he loved and trusted me for that.

The humour and jokes we have shared along the way has been amazing and continues to this day. Bart and I still argue about things, but we rarely fall out for long, there is too much honesty between us for that to happen and we usually just end up laughing about things and a funny impersonation slips out of his mouth.

He still comes home and surprises me by phoning me to find out how I am, then ringing the front door bell whilst I am chatting away to him on the telephone.

Bart has grown into a man and, to quote my close friends, "changed beyond all recognition". He is now a sensible, modest and disciplined individual who shows a maturity and personal commitment to achieve that is well beyond his years. His sense of humour is better than ever and he has great integrity, learned from all his life's previous experiences. The negative experiences he had as a child have equipped him to handle his life as an adult. Most of what life throws at him now, he takes in his stride as he has already got the T shirt and read the book!

Bart still has a way to go before he qualifies, the study is relentless and he still has many hours of practise flight ahead of him. But he is his own master now, planning his time and studying for his goal – after all the tortuous hours we studied together he is 'flying solo' in this sense.

When he achieves his goal then perhaps one day, he may be the guy whose voice comes over the flight intercom telling you your altitude and estimated time of arrival. Of course he won't be called Bart so you won't be left wondering if the guy flying the plane is the boy who once wrote "Your school sucks, Bart Nickells rules!"